BETWEEN THE PLANETS

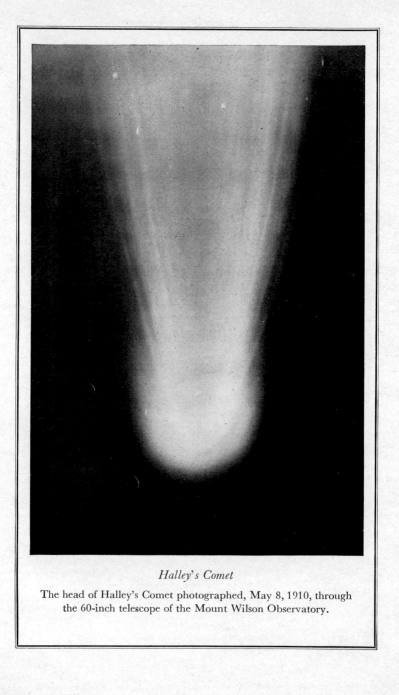

Halley's Comet

The head of Halley's Comet photographed, May 8, 1910, through
the 60-inch telescope of the Mount Wilson Observatory.

THE HARVARD BOOKS ON ASTRONOMY

Edited by

HARLOW SHAPLEY AND BART J. BOK

BETWEEN

THE

PLANETS

BY

FLETCHER G. WATSON

THE BLAKISTON COMPANY

Philadelphia · Toronto

First Edition

Copyright, September, 1941 by The Blakiston Company

Printing of October, 1945

PRINTED IN U. S. A.
THE MAPLE PRESS COMPANY, YORK, PA.

CONTENTS

1

SURVEYING THE SOLAR SYSTEM

OUR SOLAR SYSTEM, OF WHICH THE EARTH IS A MINOR
member, consists not only of the sun and nine planets, but
also of thousands of small bodies which occasionally become
far more spectacular than the brightest planet. A brilliant
comet with its tenuous tail stretching across the sky; an
asteroid swinging past the earth at a mere million miles; a
flaming fireball abruptly flood-lighting several states as it
explodes, showering meteorites on the ground below, all
dramatically reveal the usually inconspicuous small members of the solar system—occupants of the space between the
planets.

We customarily think of the solar system as a close-knit
organization of planets and their attendant satellites. Yet the
planets actually are only specks moving in a great void. If we
imagine the sun as an orange three inches across, the earth
shrinks to a mere pin-head twenty-seven feet away. On this
scale the distances of the planets from the sun and their
sizes are shown in Table 1. Compared to the distances
between them, the planets are minute. Yet interplanetary
space is not empty, for it contains a wide assortment of
wanderers which can be seen when they pass near the

TABLE 1
A Model of the Solar System

	Distance from the sun, feet	Size
Sun.....................		An orange
Mercury................	10	A grain of sand
Venus..................	19	A pin-head
Earth..................	27	Another pin-head
Mars...................	41	Another grain of sand
Jupiter.................	140	A child's marble
Saturn.................	260	A pea
Uranus.................	510	A small pill
Neptune................	800	Another pill
Pluto..................	1100	A third pin-head

earth. We distinguish them as comets, asteroids and meteors, but upon close inspection they show many characteristics in common. In this book we shall discuss these interplanetary wanderers and see what they are and to what extent they are related.

We find nearly all the little planets moving between Mars and Jupiter; many of them are very small, hardly larger than mountains whizzing around in space. Unlike them, thousands of comets, great clouds of gas and particles, move chaotically between the planets. In the paths of comets are enormous swarms of particles which dash into our atmosphere providing us with spectacular showers of shooting stars. Larger solitary masses wandering through space become flaming fireballs when they rush through the atmosphere. Fragments of the largest escape complete destruction in the air and fall to earth as meteorites—the only solid material from space that we can scrutinize and examine in the laboratory. These, the asteroids, comets, meteors and meteorites are the interplanetary wanderers, but to appreciate how they move, whence they came and what they signify, we must be familiar with the planets and their motions.

How the Planets Move

At the center of this great assembly is the sun which contains over ninety-nine per cent of all the material in the system. The planets all travel around the sun in the same direction and in paths that are nearly circular; as a result they cannot come together for neighborly visits. Seen from far above the earth's north pole the planets would appear like well-trained fire-flies moving around the sun in the counter-clockwise direction.

In addition to moving in the same direction all the planetary paths, or orbits, lie in nearly the same plane. The planetary system is a cosmic merry-go-round, in which the horses have circular orbits, move in the same direction and in nearly the same plane. There is, however, one exception; the inner planets go around the sun much more quickly than the outer planets. The period of Mercury is only eighty-eight days while that of Pluto is 248 years.

Through its gravitational attraction the sun dictates how the planets and small bodies shall move. For ages astronomers tried in vain to predict accurately the positions of the planets. Finally in 1609 Kepler, using the extensive and accurate observations of Tycho Brahe, discovered that the orbits were not circles or combinations of circles, as had previously been supposed, but were ellipses with the sun at one of the foci, at S in Figure 1. Kepler also found how the planets move along their orbits, moving fastest when they are nearest the sun, at Q, the perihelion. From these relations Newton was able to establish the law of gravitation and to show how the pull of the sun made the planets move as they do.

Elliptical orbits can be of all shapes and sizes. As a measure of their size we take half the long axis, the distance CQ in Figure 1. Within the solar system we compare all the orbital sizes to the earth's and take the distance between the sun and earth as the Astronomical Unit, A.U. As a measure of the shape of an orbit we take the ratio CS/CQ, called the eccentricity. If the sun, S, is at the center, C, the eccentricity is zero and the orbit is a circle. If, however, the sun is very near the point Q, the eccentricity is near one, the orbit is

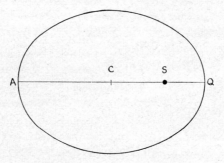

Fig. 1.—A typical ellipse.

The size and shape of an ellipse are measured by the distance CQ and the ratio CS/CQ.

very long and narrow and the aphelion, A, is far from the sun. The period required for a body to swing around the sun is determined entirely by the size of the orbit. Kepler's third relation states that the period, P, expressed in years can be found from $P^2 = a^3$ where a is half the long axis of the orbit in astronomical units. Thus Jupiter at 5.2 A.U. requires 11.9 years for a trip around the sun.

Near the end of the eighteenth century Bode was impressed by the regularity with which the planets were spaced and he devised the following scheme for representing their distances.

TABLE 2
BODE'S SCHEME FOR LOCATING THE PLANETARY ORBITS

	M	V	E	M	?	J	S	U	N	P
	.4	.4	.4	.4	.4	.4	.4	.4	.4	.4
	.0	.3	.6	1.2	2.4	4.8	9.6	19.2	38.4	76.8
Predicted.........	.4	.7	1.0	1.6	2.8	5.2	10.0	19.6	38.8	77.2
True.............	.39	.72	1.0	1.52	?	5.2	9.5	19.2	30.1	39.5 A.U.

Although this scheme gives reasonably satisfactory values through the distance of Uranus, it breaks down completely for Neptune and Pluto. Before the discovery of these two outer planets Bode's law was accepted as a very significant and fundamental relationship. If it were, the position at 2.8 A.U. should contain an undiscovered planet. This belief was held so strongly that a thorough search for it was being organized when word came in 1801 that a little planet at this solar distance had been discovered. This planet and its companions, for it is not alone, may be the fragments of a planet spoiled in the making. In Chapters 2 and 3 we shall see how they move and what they are.

VELOCITIES AND ORBITS

The velocity with which a body moves along its orbit depends upon its distance from the sun and also upon the size and shape of its orbit. Like a ball thrown into the air a body flies away from the vicinity of the sun, gradually slows down, comes momentarily to rest, then falls back toward the sun and sweeps around it to begin a new cycle. If by some magical process we could speed up a body as it moved away from the sun, it would go farther into space before turning back. A push of just the right amount would send it flying so far away it would not return for an infinite time. The orbit of a body moving in this manner has an eccentricity of exactly one and is no longer an ellipse but a parabola. At the earth's distance from the sun the velocity of a body moving in a parabola is 26.1 miles a second* and any body moving that fast or faster cannot be a permanent member of the solar system.

The chances that a body will have exactly the parabolic velocity are very small. If it moves faster, the orbit is a hyperbola having an eccentricity larger than one and, according to the mathematicians, a period of motion greater than infinity—this is just a polite way of saying that it moves off between the stars and is never seen again. We shall often mention parabolic orbits and the parabolic velocity, or the parabolic limit, which is the same thing, because they mark the dividing line between permanent members of the solar system and stray wanderers from interstellar space.

Although the planets move in nearly the same plane, comet paths are tilted or inclined at all angles; some comets move up and down across the planetary orbits just as passengers on a ferris-wheel soar far above a carnival then swoop down through the crowd. Figure 2 shows such an orbit, the comet comes up from below the earth's orbit, crosses it at the ascending node, Ω, and moves through the angle ω to perihelion.

If the planets were infinitesimal specks compared to the sun, they and the other members of the solar system would travel nicely along in the paths dictated by the sun. Jupiter and Saturn are, however, sizable bodies. Jupiter contains one thousandth as much material as the sun and Saturn contains a third as much as Jupiter. Consequently any body venturing into the vicinity of these planets will be attracted toward them by small but appreciable amounts.

---

* Or 42.1 kilometers per second.

These planetary attractions or perturbations may pull the body forward, sideways or backward in its orbit. Any such change in the direction of motion or in the velocity of a body alters its orbit and future path through space. To predict where a body will be we must know how close it can ap-

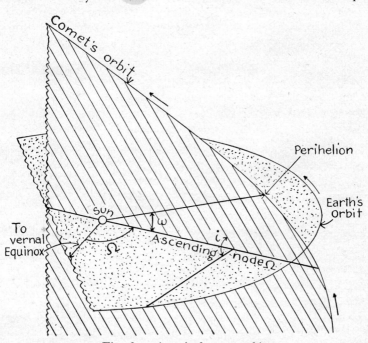

Fig. 2.—A typical comet orbit.

This comet moves up from below the earth's orbit, crosses it at the ascending node Ω and continues through the angle ω until it passes perihelion.

proach one of the planets and what happens when it does. The effects produced by the small planets like the earth and Mars are trivial, but Jupiter and Saturn do modify and even radically change the orbits of comets and asteroids that venture near.

The Metric System

Before delving into the interplanetary material we should agree upon one last matter—the units we shall use in measuring distances and weights. Two distinctly different systems of measurement are now in common use in various parts of the world. We are most familiar with the English system in which miles contain 5280 feet, feet twelve inches, pounds sixteen ounces, etc. The other system is the much simplified Metric System worked out by the French. In the Metric System each new unit is ten, a hundred or a thousand times larger or smaller than the fundamental unit. We use this system for our money—there are ten pennies in a dime and one hundred in each dollar. The basic unit of the metric system is the meter, about one ten-millionth of the distance between the earth's equator and poles. A meter, 3.280 feet, slightly exceeds the familiar English yard of three feet. A kilometer, 3280 feet, is a thousand meters, while a centimeter is one hundredth of a meter, 0.0328 feet. There are 2.54 centimeters in an inch. The fundamental unit of matter in this system is the gram, the weight of one cubic centimeter of water, approximately the contents of a thimble. A penny weighs three grams. A kilogram is a thousand grams, or 2.2 pounds, while a milligram is a thousandth of a gram. The metric system is so simple that throughout the remainder of this book we shall use it. To shift from large to small units we multiply by ten the proper number of times, that means shifting the decimal place to the right or left the proper number of places.

Now, fortified with this information about the solar system, the shapes and orientations of orbits, and the metric system, let us investigate the bodies that move between the planets.

2

THE LITTLE PLANETS

THOUSANDS OF MINOR PLANETS MOVE AROUND THE SUN, principally in the region between the orbits of Mars and Jupiter. These little bodies, when viewed through an average telescope, appear star-like and are customarily called asteroids. Despite their number the asteroids receive relatively little popular attention, chiefly because they are faint; only one of them, Vesta, is on rare occasions visible to the unaided eye. Since they are faint, move slowly across the sky, and look like stars, the first discovery of an asteroid was long delayed.

THE DISCOVERY OF ASTEROIDS

On January 1, 1801, the first day of the nineteenth century, Piazzi at Palermo, Italy, made the routine observations necessary for his catalogue of star positions. When he repeated the observations on the next night, as he customarily did to check the accuracy of his work, he noticed that one of the stars was in a different position. On the third night a further motion was evident. Piazzi thought this moving object a comet, but certainly a peculiar comet since it looked like a star while the other comets he had seen were fuzzy. He watched it for six weeks; during the first two it moved slowly westward, then stopped and returned eastward. Sudden illness interrupted Piazzi's observations and when he was able to return to his telescope he could not find the moving-star. He sent copies of his records to other observers, but the mails were very slow then and when the letters finally arrived the other astronomers searched in vain for a sight of the new object. Apparently it had been irretrievably lost.

Fortunately at this time Gauss was studying Newton's laws of motion and had derived a new method for the calculation of orbits from only a few observations. Piazzi's meager observations provided an ideal test for the new method. By it Gauss found that the orbit was similar to those of the planets and that the new body was a little planet moving in the region between Mars and Jupiter. The orbit calculated by Gauss was so accurate that on December 31, 1801, exactly a year after it was first seen, the body was relocated just a moon's diameter from the predicted position. This discovery of a new planet, at first called Ceres Ferdinandea, but soon shortened to Ceres, was a major event in astronomy, but one soon to be duplicated.

In March 1802, while searching for Ceres, Olbers discovered another moving, star-like object, later named Pallas. Gauss found that it too moved between Mars and Jupiter with about the same period as Ceres. In 1804 a third, Juno, and in 1807 a fourth, Vesta, were found, but for nearly forty years thereafter no additional ones were discovered. Finally in 1845 a fifth, somewhat fainter asteroid was added to the list and since then the number known has steadily increased. By 1891, 322 had been discovered by direct visual observation. Then Wolf, at Heidelberg, began to search for others by means of photography. As the asteroids move around the sun they gradually change their

Fig. 3.—An asteroid trail.

The asteroid reveals itself by moving during the three-hour exposure.

apparent positions among the stars. During a time-exposure of an hour or more carefully guided on the stars, the asteroids move enough to make little trails, as in Figure 3, thereby revealing themselves.

After 1891 the rate of discovery increased greatly, Table 3. Through the efforts of many observers using a variety of instruments several hundred new asteroids are now reported each year. Although the annual number of discoveries has been increasing, between forty and fifty per cent of the new objects are observed only once. Figure 4 shows the distribution of discoveries for 1930 and for 1938 according

TABLE 3

DISTRIBUTION OF ASTEROID DISCOVERIES

Years	Discovered	Numbered	Total numbered
1800–09	4	4	4
10–19	0	0	4
20–29	0	0	4
30–39	0	0	4
40–49	6	6	10
50–59	47	47	57
60–69	53	52	109
70–79	105	102	211
80–89	80	76	287
90–99	264	165	452
1900–09	776	213	665
10–19	788	249	914
20–29	1262	202	1116
30–39	2799	373	1489

to the number of observations secured and the magnitude at discovery. As we should expect, repeated observations are

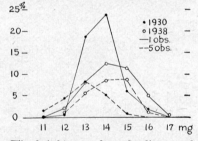

Fig. 4.—The brightness of newly-discovered asteroids.

The distribution in brightness of asteroids discovered in 1930 and 1938 shows that the more recent observations include fainter asteroids.

least frequent for the faintest bodies. With each passing year fainter bodies are found; between 1930 and 1938 the average magnitude at discovery increased from 13.5 to 14.3.

The mere discovery of a new asteroid is of relatively small value for we cannot predict its future position and locate it unless an orbit is computed. At least three accurate observations separated by several weeks are necessary if the position is to be accurately predicted for a year or more. At present only some twenty per cent of the newly discovered bodies are sufficiently observed to permit the calculation of reliable orbits. These asteroids and their orbits are numbered and entered in the register of asteroids, Kleine Planeten, which now contains over 1500 entries. To each

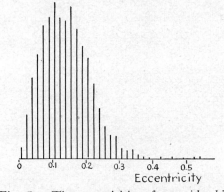

Fig. 5.—The eccentricities of asteroid orbits.

planet so recorded the discoverer may give a name. At first the names were taken from mythology. By custom those of goddesses, such as, Ceres, Pallas, Juno, and Vesta were used; but even the extensive roster of goddesses, major and minor, has been exhausted. Individuals, observatories, and cities in all parts of the earth are now commemorated in the heavens. With the exceptions of the Trojan group and a few others having unusual orbits the names are put in the feminine form, as Piazzia, Pittsburghia, and Utopia.

Observers, both amateur and professional, in many countries contribute to the growing list of asteroids. Reinmuth at

Heidelberg has a tremendously impressive total of 980
discoveries, of which some are rediscoveries and some single
observations. Even so 189 of them have been numbered and
entered in Kleine Planeten. Wolf's total of 582 discoveries is
hardly half as large as Reinmuth's but Wolf contributed the
most, 228, that received numbers.

How Asteroids Move

Before attempting to find out what kind of objects asteroids really are we shall study how they move relative to the
planets. Unlike the planets the asteroids move in orbits
which are appreciably elongated. A typical asteroid orbit
appears in Figure 6. Such an orbit is nearly a circle, but with
the sun off-center; between perihelion and aphelion the
distance from the sun to the orbit varies by thirty per cent.
Hidalgo (944) is noted as having the largest and the most
eccentric orbit. With a semi-major axis of 5.80 A.U. and an
eccentricity of 0.656, it moves from perihelion at 2.0 A.U.
not far beyond the orbit of Mars, to aphelion at 9.6 A.U.,
nearly the distance of Saturn. As a result of this great
change in distance its brightness varies during the 13.9 year
period from the tenth magnitude at which it is readily
observed, to the nineteenth magnitude where it could barely
be located with the largest telescopes.

The periods of the asteroid motions are distributed in a
very irregular and interesting manner. According to Figure
7 only a few require more than six or less than three and a
half years for a trip around the sun. In the distribution of
periods there are several large gaps whose significance we
shall later discuss in detail.

In their orbital eccentricities ana inclinations, Figures 5
and 8, the asteroids avoid exact similarity with the major
planets. The average eccentricity of an orbit is 0.15 and the
average inclination 9°.7. Only a few lie near the plane of the

earth's motion while several are tilted at large angles. Despite the considerable range in inclination not one of the 1500 bodies moves around the sun in the direction opposite to the major planets; in this respect the asteroids are typical

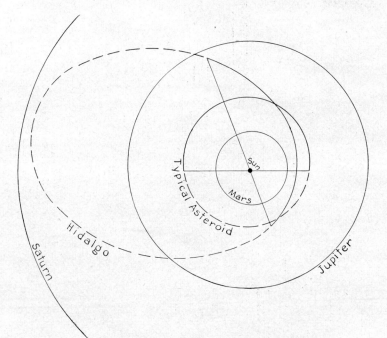

Fig. 6.—Orbits of a typical asteroid and of Hidalgo.

Along the dashed line the asteroids are below the plane of the earth's motion. The orbit of a typical asteroid is tilted 10° while that of Hidalgo is tilted 42.5°.

planets. Due to the moderate inclinations of their orbits the majority of asteroids usually remain in the zodiacal band. Any new one found far from the zodiac is immediately subjected to close scrutiny for its orbit may be highly inclined or the body quite near the earth.

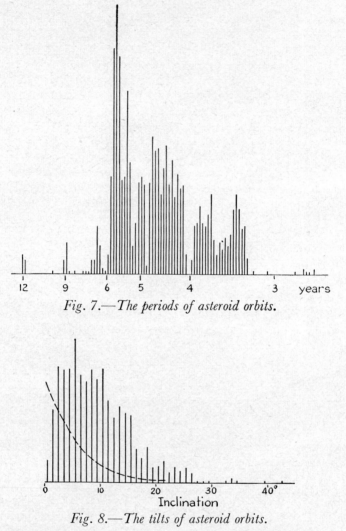

Fig. 7.—The periods of asteroid orbits.

Fig. 8.—The tilts of asteroid orbits.

The majority of asteroid orbits are inclined several degrees to the plane of the earth's motion. The dashed line shows the distribution after correction for the chances that an orbit will have a low inclination; small tilts are relatively frequent.

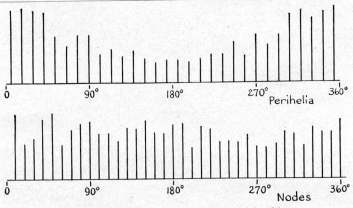

Fig. 9.—*The orientation of asteroid orbits.*

Upper: how the perihelion positions of asteroid orbits are turned with respect to the long axis of Jupiter's orbit. Lower: The directions in which asteroid orbits cross the earth's orbital plane.

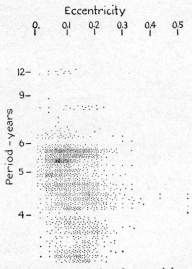

Fig. 10.—*Relation between period and eccentricity of asteroid orbits.*

In 1862 Newcomb noticed that the perihelia of asteroid orbits were concentrated on one side of the sun. While part of this arrangement may be due to seasonal influences affecting the likelihood of discovery, much of it is due to a tendency for the asteroid orbits to parallel Jupiter's, as shown by Figure 9.

By comparing the orbital elements two at a time we can see to what extent their irregularities are associated. The pattern in Figure 10 shows in detail how eccentricity de-

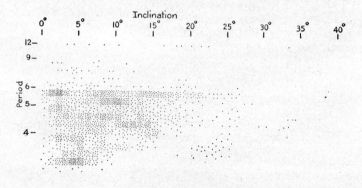

Fig. 11.—Relation between period and inclination of asteroid orbits.

pends upon period. Of the long-period asteroids we might expect to discover only those having eccentric orbits. Actually the reverse occurs for, with the exception of Hidalgo, the eccentricities of the large orbits are consistently small. In a similar manner Figure 11 exhibits the dependence of inclination upon period. Here again the variation of the distribution reveals a striking interdependence; especially noticeable is the scarcity of large inclinations for periods less than 3.6 years. For the periods between seven and ten years the inclinations are all low while for periods near twelve years the orbital tilts are widely scattered. Thus the shapes and orientation of the asteroid orbits depend upon their periods, which in turn measure rather accurately the closeness with which they approach the orbit of massive Jupiter.

JUPITER'S DOMINATION

The extent to which the asteroid orbits are arranged by Jupiter is most clearly demonstrated by the irregularities or gaps in the frequency of their periods. The most conspicuous gaps occur at 5.9, 4.8 and 4.0 years—exactly one-half, two-fifths and one-third the period of Jupiter. Other depressions in Figure 7 mark orbits whose periods are one-fourth, one-fifth, three-fifths and three-sevenths Jupiter's. Such orbits in which the periods are exact fractions of some larger period are called resonant orbits, similar to the overtones of a musical note. If we strike a piano note, a properly tuned violin string will start to sing because it picks up the tone to which it is tuned. The violin string makes one vibration as each sound wave passes and is exactly ready to be pushed aside again by the next wave. Other notes do not find the violin ready or sympathetic and cannot make it sing. Another familiar example of resonance is pumping a swing. We always apply the push at the same part of the arc and in the same direction, thereby overcoming the tendency for the swing to die. Similarly with the motions of asteroids, those in tune or in resonance with Jupiter move in peculiar ways. The steady monotonous pull of the great planet each time they pass it in the same part of their path sets up rhythmic changes in the asteroid motions and eventually forces them into peculiar orbits. The great singer Caruso knew well how devastating the effects of a beat period or resonance could be. He would sing the natural tone of a glass goblet until it began to vibrate. As he sang louder and louder the goblet vibrated more and more until finally the ever-increasing vibrations shattered it.

The mathematical theory of how and why such resonant motion produces the observed results is very complex and not completely worked out. According to the simplified investigations of Bessel and Newcomb, orbit groupings might be expected where gaps are observed. Recently E. W. Brown discussed more thoroughly the orbits with periods of six years. He found that neither their sizes nor shapes could remain fixed and that periods within twenty-five days of the critical value must change rapidly. At any time few asteroids can have periods within this zone. The position and size of this gap is confirmed by the observations. How and why groupings occur at periods of eight and nine years, where the orbits are remarkable for their low inclinations, remains a perplexing and unsolved problem.

Although the mathematical study of resonant motion is complicated and incomplete, the location of the gaps exactly at the proper places leaves no doubt they are formed through the accumulated effects of many Jovian perturbations. Certainly the present arrangement of these well-shuffled orbits can tell little or nothing about the positions and motions of the asteroids two billion years ago when the solar system was newly-formed.

Those asteroids having approximately the same period as Jupiter form an unusually interesting group called the Trojans. Long ago the famous French astronomer Lagrange found that three bodies situated at the corners of an equilateral triangle and describing orbits of the same size were in an equilibrium configuration and would not greatly change their relative positions. Many years later, in 1904, Wolf discovered an asteroid near one of the triangular positions with respect to Jupiter and the sun, Figure 12. Since then others have been discovered and now twelve are known. Figures 10 and 11 show that the orbits of the Trojans have small eccentricities and large inclinations.

Lagrange's ideal arrangement failed to consider the gravitational attraction of the other planets. As a consequence of the pull of Saturn the Trojans occasionally wander far from their equilateral positions. Under certain conditions they could approach quite close to Jupiter whereupon their orbits may be radically changed and they lose their membership in the group. Conversely, given just the proper circumstances, an asteroid might be captured by Jupiter and become a Trojan. Thus membership in this group is probably not permanent, but only one of long tenure. The best chances for capture seem to be from orbits with periods slightly greater than the critical values. Possibly the asteroids originated in the zone between Jupiter and Saturn and many are still there, but so far from the sun and so faint that we do not discover them.

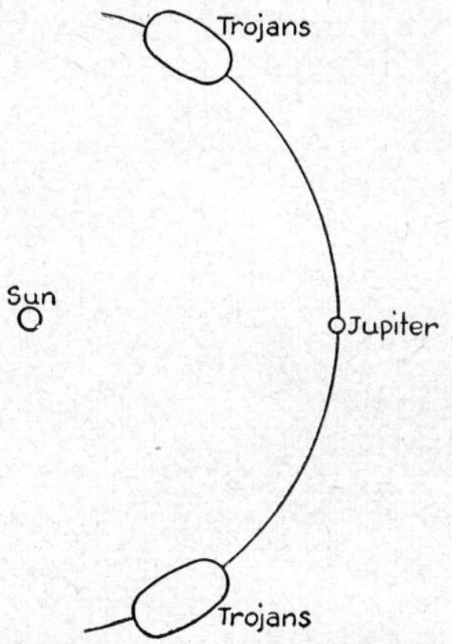

Fig. 12.—*The Trojan asteroids.*

The Trojans are at Jupiter's distance from the sun, but 60° ahead of or behind that planet.

All attempts to estimate the interval required for the asteroids and planets to reach their present orbital configurations have been unsatisfactory. Through the combination of recurring perturbations certain changes in the orbits are periodic and over long intervals of time vary within limits. Other changes are progressive, continually increasing with time, and after great intervals produce important differences in the arrangement of the orbits. From observations covering at most a few thousand years the rates of only the short-period and largest progressive terms can be accurately evaluated for the massive major planets whose orbits change slowly. When we attempt to compute their orbits millions of years ago, the small uncertainties are multiplied by thousands and we can formulate no picture of the planetary arrangement at intervals more than a hundred million years ago. For the tiny asteroids that repeatedly pass near Jupiter our view into the past blurs more rapidly.

SIZE AND BRIGHTNESS

How bright an asteroid appears to us depends upon its size, upon its distances from the sun and earth and upon the angle at which it reflects the sunlight we see. A small body near the earth looks as bright and has the same chance of being discovered as a large body at the distance of Jupiter. Since nearly all the asteroids appear as points of light, we must determine their sizes through their brightness. If we know their distances from the sun and earth, we can compute what their brightnesses, or absolute magnitudes, would be at one astronomical unit from the sun and earth and pick out the large bodies because they are brightest. The brightnesses are expressed in the scale of magnitudes where numerically large magnitudes represent faint bodies, just as a sixth magnitude star is fainter than one of the first magnitude. Two asteroids that differ by five magnitudes have a hundred-fold difference in brightness as well as surface area and consequently a ten-fold difference in radius.

The earliest discoveries included the brightest bodies which could be either small and near by or large and distant. In Figure 13 the frequencies of absolute magnitudes are arranged according to intervals in the period and the order of discovery. For distant bodies having periods greater than six years discovery is still incomplete at absolute magnitude eight, while for periods less than four years incompleteness does not begin before magnitude eleven or possibly twelve.

From Figure 13 we may estimate the number of small asteroids. For absolute magnitude seven or less the total count of 199 is nearly complete over all periods. For the interval at eighth magnitude we may estimate the number, when complete, as about 330, and thus obtain a total of 530 with absolute magnitudes brighter than nine. Over these

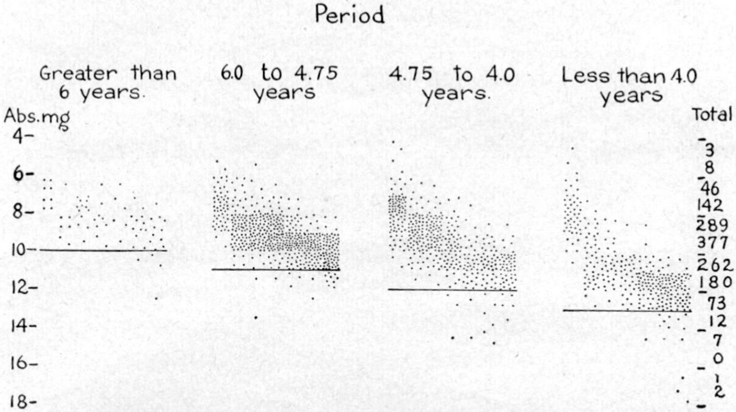

Period

Greater than 6 years	6.0 to 4.75 years	4.75 to 4.0 years	Less than 4.0 years	

Abs.mg

				Total
4–				‾3
6–				8
				‾46
8–				142
				‾289
10–				377
				‾262
12–				180
				‾73
14–				‾12
16–				‾7
				‾0
18–				‾2

Fig. 13.—The absolute magnitudes of 1400 asteroids.

These magnitudes have been grouped according to period and order of discovery; early discoveries are at the left and recent ones at the right in each group. The distribution of the dots shows that we have discovered all the large asteroids of short period, but are still finding those of similar size far from the sun. The cross lines mark the fifteenth apparent magnitude.

magnitudes the number of asteroids increase rapidly with faintness, approximately 2.7 times with each magnitude step. The number of faint asteroids yet to be discovered must be very large; with the increase-factor 2.7 the number with absolute magnitudes between nine and ten awaiting discovery nearly equals the total now catalogued.

With the methods now in use, the derivation of precise orbits for all these faint asteroids will involve a great amount of labor. Already we are near the saturation point in this work, for only a few dozen orbits are derived each year although hundreds of new bodies are discovered. In addition to working out the new orbits we must continually correct all the old ones for the perturbations of Jupiter and Saturn. There are, however, two encouraging developments in computational technique. Special types of electrical computing machines, consisting of many separate units wired together like a spiderweb, are being devised and they may take over much of the routine work within the near future. Another labor-saving method for the prediction of positions is offered by the technique tested at the Students' Observatory of the University of California. General perturbations—tabulated quantities which yield for any orbit the corrections necessary for the particular circumstances—have been investigated and found to yield positions sufficiently accurate for identification after several years. Since this is the goal of the calculations we may expect the extensive use of general perturbations to reduce appreciably the effort necessary to keep account of these hundreds of bodies.

We have already seen how small bodies near the earth may be discovered while large bodies far away pass unnoticed. From Figure 13 we can get some idea of the true number of asteroids at various distances from the sun. Down to absolute magnitude eight our discovery seems to be rather complete. In Table 4 we compare the numbers

TABLE 4

PERIODS OF ASTEROIDS WITH ABSOLUTE MAGNITUDES BRIGHTER THAN EIGHT

Period in years	Greater than 6	6–4.75	4.75–4.0	Less than 4.0
Number..........	27	72	72	28
Per cent..........	14	36	36	14

known in various zones. Apparently the asteroidal frequency is nearly symmetrical about periods of 4.75 years. Five per cent of the 199 large asteroids are Trojans which suggests that five per cent of all the asteroids may be Trojans.

Another indication of the number of faint asteroids can be gained from photographs made with large telescopes. Baade, using the one hundred-inch reflector at the Mount Wilson Observatory, observed the number of asteroids within the zodiac and estimated that there should be 44,000 asteroids brighter than the nineteenth apparent magnitude. From similar observations Hubble estimated the number as 30,000. The distribution of absolute magnitudes and solar distances leads us to expect about eighty thousand brighter than the nineteenth photographic magnitude. The agreement between our prediction and the observational results is none too good, but neither figure is precise. Certainly the number of small, faint asteroids is very great.

How much matter floats through the solar system in the form of asteroids can only be estimated. We can add up all the observed asteroids and see what they amount to, and we can compute what effect they would have on the planets if they totaled a certain amount. Using the later method we find that if their total mass were a sixth of that of the earth, they would produce changes in the motion of Mars. But since the predicted changes do not occur, the total mass of the asteroids must be less than that of the earth, probably even less than that of the moon.

While attempting to account for the asteroids, Hirayama began a search for indications of a common origin through the existence of asteroid families. Among the orbital elements the great variety and continual variation seem to mask any clues. Hirayama found, however, certain combinations of the elements that would not change appreciably despite perturbations during centuries. Searching among more than a thousand orbits he found nearly two hundred which seem to form five loose groups or families. How important these families are and what they signify still remain to be determined.

Asteroids That Pass Near

Several small asteroids that pass near the earth deserve special mention. The first asteroid found to cross inside the orbit of Mars was Eros (433) discovered in 1898 by Witt at Berlin. Eros was immediately the center of much attention since at the most favorable times it approaches within 23,-000,000 kilometers of the earth. At this small distance it provides an accurate way to measure the distance between the earth and sun, the astronomical unit. When the distance to Eros is least, its position among the stars will differ by a whole minute of arc as seen from opposite sides of the earth. From precise measurements the differences in position as seen from various observatories can be found and since the distances between the observatories are known the distance to Eros can be found. From its orbit the distance can be computed in astronomical units and a comparison of the two results gives the astronomical unit in kilometers. At present this unit is known within a tenth of one per cent, but a more accurate value would be welcomed because the astronomical unit is the fundamental yardstick used in measuring all celestial distances.

In 1932 Delporte in Belgium discovered another close-approaching asteroid with an erratic orbit; in keeping with the erotic tradition it was named Amor (1221). Sufficient observations were obtained to give a reliable orbit and in 1940 he recovered the object only a few degrees from the predicted position. In the interval it had made three trips around the sun and was once again favorably situated near the earth. Albert (719) also has its perihelion in the zone between the earth and Mars, but it has never been seen since the time of discovery in 1911.

On April 27, 1932 Reinmuth at Heidelberg discovered a rapidly moving body, Apollo, which passed much nearer the earth than did either Eros or Amor. The least separation was

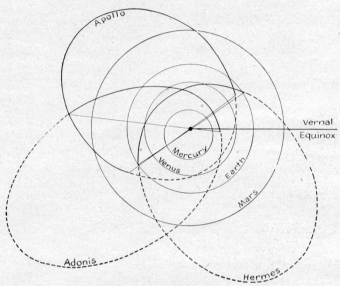

Fig. 14.—The orbits of Apollo, Adonis and Hermes.

All three move in orbits inclined only a few degrees to the earth's orbit and come up across it where their paths are marked by solid lines.

a mere three million kilometers—almost too close for comfort. From the few observations gathered before the little body faded from sight the orbit was computed and found to have a period of only 1.8 years and to pass inside the orbits of the earth and Venus. That Apollo was not a solitary vagabond thrown into such an orbit by a close approach to Mars was soon evident, for on February 12, 1936 Delporte and again on October 28, 1937 Reinmuth discovered other

objects called Adonis and Hermes having similar motions in
rather eccentric orbits of low inclination.

Adonis passed the earth at one and a half million kilometers, while Hermes came closer, possibly as near as a
million kilometers, less than three times the distance to the

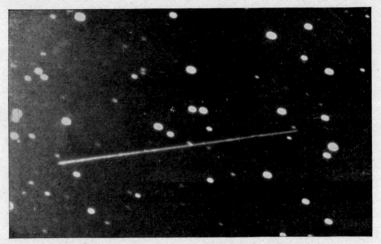

Fig. 15.—The discovery photograph of Hermes.

Although the telescope was moved during the exposure to make
ordinary asteroids appear as circular dots, Hermes was moving so fast
it resembles a meteor trail.

moon. The recent discovery of this group of bodies is a great
compliment to the alertness of modern observers and to their
photographic technique. The difficulties of discovery and
observation are shown by the fact that when the discovery
of Hermes was telegraphed around the world many people
attempted to photograph it, but not one succeeded for it
moved at such a rate that it was many degrees ahead of
them. On October 30, 1937 when it shot past the earth,
Hermes was of the eighth magnitude and moving five degrees an hour. In spite of its brightness no image could be
found on several photographs known to cover its position. In

nine days it moved completely across the sky. The effect was much like that obtained by standing near the railroad tracks when the evening express roars past. The only observations available for the determinations of its orbit were from photographs taken for other purposes before the asteroid was discovered. Unfortunately Adonis, Apollo and Hermes were observed for such short times that their orbits are very uncertain. There is little hope that they will be observed again except by accident when they happen to pass near the earth during some future dash around the sun.

These little bodies, just one or two kilometers across, can be observed only when they are very near the earth. But to pass near the earth they must have orbits oriented in a very special manner such that they cross the plane of the earth's motion when they are near the earth's distance from the sun. Thus the chances of discovering one of them is small and the three we know must represent several hundreds, possibly thousands, of tiny bodies with similar orbits.

When these cosmic bullets swing past at a mere million kilometers we start worrying about the likelihood of collision. The earth's radius is only 6370 kilometers and the chances that a body scheduled to pass within a million kilometers will score a direct hit on the earth is about one in thirty thousand. Close approaches by these flying mountains are rare and the earth probably goes at least a hundred thousand years between collisions with them. Yet there may be myriads of smaller bodies travelling in similar orbits. As we shall see in later chapters, sizable bodies do strike the earth every few thousand years and millions of small particles dash into our atmosphere each day.

3

WHIRLING FRAGMENTS

What are asteroids? To answer this question we must interpret the light they send us in every possible man-

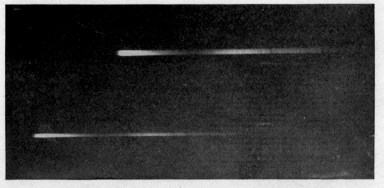

Fig. 16.—The light of Vesta and a star.

The light of Vesta (above) has been dispersed by a prism, red on the left, and photographed on a panchromatic film. Below is the spectrum of a star cooler and redder than the sun. The break in the middle of the spectra results from the relative insensitivity of the film to green light.

ner, for we cannot get a close view of them. Their distance does, however, lend the enchantment of mystery. The light we receive from the asteroids is like that from the moon or any other cold solid mass revealed only by reflected sunlight. But small changes in the intensity and color of the light depend upon the nature and composition of the reflecting surfaces; from these subtle changes we must derive whatever information we can about the nature of the asteroids.

Through the largest telescopes experienced observers can just see the four brightest asteroids as tiny disks. Even when they are closest to the earth the disks are only a few tenths of a second of arc across, the size of a penny at ten or fifteen kilometers. Ceres, the largest asteroid, is 770 kilometers across, less than a fourth the diameter of the moon. The small size of Vesta, Table 5, is surprising, for it has an absolute magnitude equal to that of Ceres. Evidently Vesta has an unusually high reflecting power.

TABLE 5

CHARACTERISTICS OF THE LARGEST ASTEROIDS, MERCURY AND THE MOON

Object	Diameter, km.	Absolute magnitude	p	q	Albedo
Ceres............	770	3.70	0.10	0.55	0.06
Pallas............	490	4.38	.13	.55	.07
Juno.............	193	5.74	.22	.55	.12
Vesta............	386	3.50	.48	.55	.26
Mercury..........	5000	−0.88	.164	.42	.069
Moon.............	3476	0.40	.124	.584	.073

Because we cannot directly measure the sizes of the fainter and smaller asteroids, we must use their absolute magnitudes as an indication of size. Their reflecting powers differ, but

TABLE 6

ASTEROID SIZE AND ABSOLUTE MAGNITUDE

Absolute magnitude........	5.0	10.0	15.0	20.0
Diameter in kilometers......	270	27	2.7	0.27

we assume a representative value, that of Juno, and calculate what sizes correspond to various absolute magnitudes. The majority of catalogued asteroids, having absolute magnitudes of eight, nine, and ten, are less than a hundred kilometers across. With this scale of sizes, we can see how large a body all the asteroids would make if they constituted a single mass. Bodies that differ by one in absolute magnitude differ in volume by a factor of four. But the number of small bodies increases only 2.7 times with each magnitude so for each fainter magnitude interval the total mass is only $2.7 \times \frac{1}{4} = 0.68$ times that in the next brighter interval. Consequently the faint asteroids add but a vanishingly small fraction to the total mass. By changing the brightnesses into sizes and summing, we find that all the asteroids would make a body only about five times as large as Juno, a sphere a thousand kilometers in diameter. The total mass of such a body would be about one four-thousandth that of the earth, far too small to be detectable through its gravitational attraction on Mars.

THEIR REFLECTING POWERS

Since the asteroids are little solid bodies visible by reflected sunlight in the same way as the moon, we might well inquire into the peculiarities of moonlight. The most obvious lunar effect is its change with phase as it waxes and wanes each month. Careful measurements show that the quarter-moon sends us only one-ninth as much light as the full-moon. The full-moon, directly opposite the sun in the sky, is a much better reflector than the quarter moon and the moon's brightness decreases rapidly as the angle at which we see it changes from full-phase, Figure 17. The asteroids far out in space treat light similarly, but because they stay outside the orbit of Mars, they are always seen near full-phase; the largest departures are rarely more than

30°, Figure 18. Yet after we allow for their changing solar and terrestrial distances this angle is sufficient to introduce a change of nearly a magnitude in their brightness.

The rate of magnitude change with phase-angle, the phase-coefficient, depends upon the shape of the body, whether flat, spherical or irregular, and upon the nature of

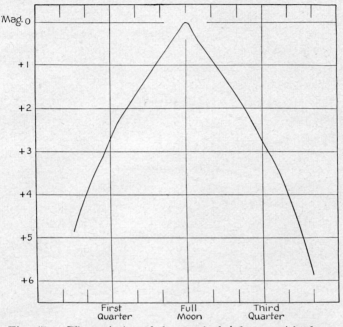

Fig. 17.—The variation of the moon's brightness with phase.

its surface, whether smooth or pitted. Attempts to predict the phase-coefficients of planets and asteroids on the basis of assumed shapes and surfaces have met with little success. Our best comparison is with the moon which can be observed through almost all phases. Over the small phase angles at which they are observed the magnitudes of asteroids, like the moon, change uniformly with the angle. The average value for thirty-four asteroids is 0.030 magnitudes per degree. Over the same angles the coefficient for the moon is 0.028 and for Mercury 0.032. Mars and Venus, planets with atmospheres, have lower values near 0.015 and recently Danjon at Strasbourg, through a study of earth-

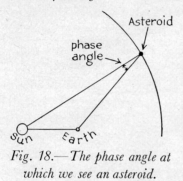

light reflected from the dark of the crescent moon, found a similar value of 0.0156 for the earth's coefficient. This distinction between the bodies with and without atmospheres places the asteroids among the members of our solar system not encased in protective lay-ers of gas. This result is not surprising for the asteroids are

Fig. 18.—The phase angle at which we see an asteroid.

smaller than the moon which itself is not massive enough to prevent the gas atoms of an atmosphere from escaping.

Irrespective of what shapes the asteroids actually have, we can hardly conceive of them as flat surfaces like those generally studied in laboratories. For this reason the fraction of light reflected by the asteroids is customarily called the *albedo*, while the term *reflectivity* is reserved for the description of flat surfaces. Any theoretical definition of the albedo is complicated by the variations of brightness with phase angle; the only practical definition is based upon observation. The fraction of the incident sunlight reflected toward the earth from an asteroid depends upon the reflectivity of its surface and upon the effects of the phase angle. We denote the reflectivity by a quantity p, and the effects of phase by a quantity q^*. The value of the albedo A, is then $A = p \times q$. The value of p can be determined only for

---

* For definitions of p and q see H. N. Russell, *Astrophysical Journal* 43, pp. 101 and 173, 1916.

the large asteroids whose sizes we can observe; in Table 5 the values of p range from 0.10 to 0.48. Some are fairly dark while others are very good reflectors and would appear white.

The color of a material is often related to its chemical composition. For example, certain rocks containing iron oxides are grey or black, but upon heating they take up more oxygen and become rusty red. Through the study of colors of asteroids we hope to determine what terrestrial materials they resemble and whether they treat light in the same manner as meteorites, which may have been little asteroids before they encountered the earth.

There are two techniques by which we can measure the color of a star or an asteroid. Both depend upon the fact that white light is really a mixture of all colors in definite proportions. With a prism we disperse the colors, spreading them out into a spectrum which may be permanently recorded upon photographic plates sensitive to long ranges of color. By carefully comparing such spectrograms of asteroids and of stars like the sun we determine how nearly alike their light really is. Because the spectra are wasteful of light and this technique involves much careful work, the results are few and are limited to the brighter asteroids. Another index to the colors of fainter asteroids can be derived from direct photographs taken through blue and red color-filters; a reddish body appears brighter in red light than it does in blue. By comparisons with stars whose colors are known the colors of asteroids can be measured rather accurately. Investigations on the colors of asteroids are not numerous, but they indicate that few if any of them reflect more blue light then red, which means that they have greyish or perhaps slightly brownish surfaces.

For comparison with the asteroids, only one study of rock colors in which forty-seven materials were examined by

Wilsing and Scheiner* is available. Although the results are
not of high precision, they indicate what might be expected
of almost any type of rock. Every specimen reflected more
yellow light than blue and only three returned a fraction less
red light than blue. These results indicate that asteroids are
slightly brownish, like nearly all natural terrestrial materials. Bluish asteroids must be rare and of uncommon
composition.

Variable Asteroids

While observing Eros in 1900 von Oppolzer was astonished to find it changing greatly in brightness. Within 79
minutes it dropped a magnitude and a half. During the next
hours it brightened to the original magnitude, only to wane
again. A whole period, including two maxima and two
minima, required but 5h 16m. This unusual behavior
attracted much attention, but the wonder soon increased
as the great variation died away and within a few months
disappeared. Thereafter when Eros came near the earth it
was watched for a recurrence of the variation. Sometimes
none was present, frequently it could be barely detected, but
occasionally the extreme range appeared. Thus the mystery
deepened.

Evidently the short-period variation results because Eros
is rotating rapidly. The little mass may have light and dark
hemispheres, like the rompers of a circus clown. Or it may
be two small fragments of rock spinning around their common center of mass and sometimes eclipsing each other. A
more flexible model, one that can be adapted to account for
all the observations, makes Eros a long, thin, irregularily-
shaped body, like a rough brick, rotating about an axis
nearly perpendicular to the greatest dimension. At times the

---

*Publications of the Potsdam Observatory, *20*, #4, 1909, and *24*, #4, 1921.

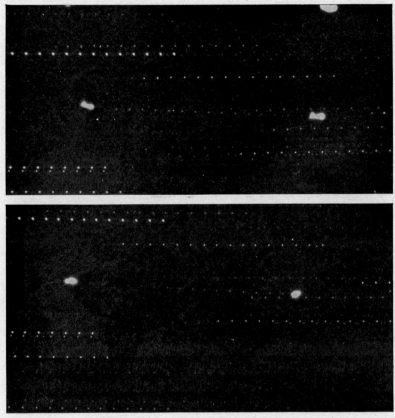

Fig. 19.—The variation of Eros.

On January 28, 1938 Eros was moving southward rapidly and varying by more than one magnitude. The Figure shows two multiple
exposure photographs, with the sets of images of Eros marked. Each
exposure was six minutes long, the first of each series being at the left.
During the first series, top picture, Eros faded rapidly. Its brightness
reached a minimum at the start of the second series and then increased
again.

earth and Eros are so situated that as it rotates we continually see only the top or bottom with no change in
brightness. More frequently we are near its equatorial
plane and see alternately part of the ends and sides as well

as the top or bottom with small variations. Occasionally we are in line with the equator of Eros. Then ends and sides are alternately visible and the variations are greatest. Early in February 1938 the earth was due to pass through the equatorial plane of Eros and large variations were expected to appear. Observations during January and February of that year confirmed our expectations, for the variation of Eros increased to the expected maximum of one and a half magnitudes near the predicted time, Figure 19.

In 1931 when the distance between the earth and Eros was nearly the least possible, van den Bos and Finsen, experienced double-star observers at Johannesburg, observed its size and watched it rotate in the same direction as the planets. From the observed size, the length must be about twenty-two kilometers and the diameter six kilometers. Minor differences in the light variation between successive periods strongly suggests that the surface is not smooth, but quite irregular. We can best explain the behavior of Eros by considering it a whirling fragment, a spinning splinter.

After the large variations of Eros and their strange occurrence at certain times had been discovered, other asteroids were watched for similar behavior. Of seventy-four studied by Miss Harwood eighteen have at one time or another certainly undergone appreciable variations while others are suspected of similar behavior. Twelve of the eighteen have periods ranging between two and twelve hours. The others were insufficiently observed to reveal their periods or they vary in such erratic manners, due perhaps to large surface irregularities, that no periods could be found. One of the most enigmatic asteroids is Vesta which shows small variations of an extremely erratic character. If all the asteroids could be observed with sufficient accuracy, a large fraction, if not all, would at some time probably show variations.

USING POLAROID

The last way of handling light to make it tell us about the asteroids involves the now-common material Polaroid. Reflected light, such as that from the planets and asteroids, differs from the incident sun-light in being polarized. Ordinary light consists of vibrations equally frequent in all directions, but upon being reflected the vibrations become less frequent in one direction than in that perpendicular. By using Polaroid, or some similar material like Iceland Spar crystals, the degree of polarization can be measured; it depends strongly upon the phase-angle at which the light is reflected and upon the nature of the reflecting surface. Lyot accurately measured the percentage of polarized light from the moon, the planets, many terrestrial materials and from Vesta. The moon, Mercury and Vesta gave essentially the same results over small phase-angles. We conclude once again that their surfaces are essentially similar in nature.

The nature of the moon's surface has been studied extensively by Lyot and by F. E. Wright. From polarization measurements combined with our knowledge of how fast the moon's surface cools when it is eclipsed, they conclude that the moon is covered with a layer of some porous material similar to volcanic ash. We might not be surprised to find ash on the moon or Mercury, but tiny Vesta could hardly have supported volcanoes. The porous material on it probably consists of dust and fragments resulting from the impact of meteors on the unprotected surface of the asteroid.

ORIGIN OF ASTEROIDS

This chapter is titled "Whirling Fragments," a term which summarizes our knowledge of the asteroids while suggesting a catastrophic origin for them. Short period

variations in brightness must mean that the asteroids are
rotating, spotted or irregularly-shaped bodies. On a spotted
body the light and dark areas will generally show not only
differences in reflectivity but also differences in color. The
actual occurrence of such color changes is doubtful, for
precise measurements of Vesta, Figure 20, and Eros show no

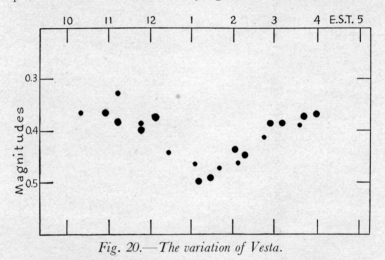

Fig. 20.—The variation of Vesta.

On Oct. 15–16, 1939 Vesta varied by 0.15 magnitudes. The large dots
refer to photographic observations in blue light and the small dots to
more accurate photoelectric observations in infra-red light made by
Green and Hall at Amherst. Vesta varied by the same amount in each
color, thereby indicating that its variation is not due to a change of
color.

color changes during the light variations. Hence we conclude that spottiness plays a minor role in producing the
variation, while irregularities in shape are the principal
causes. Any body solidifying in space under its own gravitational attraction will assume a spherical shape. Even the
effects of rapid rotation are not sufficient to account for the
irregularities in shape that exist among the asteroids. We

must conclude then that these little bodies are the whirling fragments of some celestial catastrophe.

Where, and when such a catastrophe took place, what was disrupted and how, are questions that tax our imagination. The orbital arrangement of the asteroids suggests that possibly an interval of several hundred million years was required for establishing the present organization. Frequent suggestions make asteroids the remains of a missing planet that, according to Bode's law, should be found in the zone between Mars and Jupiter. Some evidence, especially the probable large number of Trojans, hints that the asteroids originated in the zone between Jupiter and Saturn, or even farther out in the system.

Because some of the asteroids move in orbits like those of the short-period comets a genetic relationship between them has been suggested. In the following chapters about comets and meteor streams we shall see that the comets and asteroids differ greatly in nature. The similarities noted are only orbital and might be anticipated, since the motions of asteroids and short-period comets are both dominated by the perturbations of Jupiter.

Until there is reason to believe otherwise, we can proceed on the hypothesis that all the asteroids came from the same parent body which did not exceed the earth in size. Several modes of disruption are possible. First, it may have blown up because heat collected internally and could not escape. This seems unlikely. Radioactive disintegration is the only known source of such heat and to produce enough heat for disruption the planet should have been nearly pure radioactive stuff, hardly like any of the planets existing now. Even if it had such a composition, the mass would be more likely to melt than burst. Collision between a small planet and a satellite of Jupiter is not an impossibility. The results of such a collision would be similar to those from tidal disintegration.

If a satellite, say the moon, ventures within a certain distance of a larger mass, like the earth, the gravitational attraction of the large mass will become so intense that it will pull the nearer side of the satellite away from the farther side—thereby completely disrupting it. With a satellite, which remains near the disrupter, the process will continue until the fragments become so small that their internal cohesion overcomes the disruptive force. The rings about Saturn probably originated in this manner. A small planet wandering close past a much larger one, like Jupiter, could be torn apart by the disruptive forces, but the fragments would escape before they suffered further disintegration. Parts of the original small planet might be thrown into hyperbolic orbits and lost to the system while other portions might be captured by the large planet as satellites. Many of the fragments would, however, escape both fates and continue to swing around the sun in orbits much like those of their progenitor, subject to the dominating perturbations of the large planet. Such may have been the origin of the asteroids.

4

COMETS IN MOTION

*F*ROM PREHISTORIC TIMES MEN HAVE BEEN AWED BY THE appearance of great comets whose tails stretched far across the sky. For ages such comets were thought to be merely clouds in the atmosphere. Tycho Brahe found, however, that the Comet of 1577 had the same position among the stars when seen from Prague and from his observatory on the island of Hveen in the Baltic Sea and was therefore more distant than the moon and a fit subject for real astronomical study.

Comets seemed to move across the sky mysteriously, helter-skelter in any direction at changing speeds. Attempting to account for such motions Tycho assigned the comet of 1577 to a circular orbit outside that of Venus while his pupil, Kepler, thought comets moved through space along straight lines. Halley finally solved the problem of their motion in his treatise on comets published in 1705. Using Newton's recently propounded theory of gravitation Halley calculated parabolic orbits for twenty-four bright comets and found those of 1531, 1607 and 1682 to be strikingly similar. These he concluded must be reappearances of the same comet moving around the sun with a period of seventy-

five or seventy-six years. The variations of the period he correctly attributed to the attractions of the major planets. Halley predicted that the comet would reappear about 1758, but he did not live to see his bold prediction gloriously fulfilled. By the time the comet was due the planetary attractions affecting the path could be calculated with some precision; Clairaut found they would delay its appearance by some six hundred days. On Christmas Day 1758 an amateur astronomer located the comet once again nearing the sun after a trip which had carried it beyond the orbit of Neptune. Soon all the world was watching it swing past perihelion only a month from the date predicted by Clairaut. Thus Halley proved that at least some comets are permanent members of the solar system.

Fig 21.—Halley's Comet May 6, 1910.

Within the tail are many fine streamers and spikes. (*Lick Observatory.*)

Now it is known through historical research that this comet has been observed and recorded many times during the past centuries. In the Chinese and Japanese annals it can be identified at every appearance except one since 240 B.C.

Fig. 22.—Comet 1941c on February 19, 1941.

This comet appeared in the morning sky far south of the sun, then moved between the earth and sun and became briefly visible to the unaided eye from northern latitudes. Its orbital motion quickly carried it away from the earth and the comet faded rapidly. (*Perkins Observatory.*)

In 1818 Encke found that the faint comets observed in 1786, 1795, 1805 and 1818 were reappearances of the same comet which was moving around the sun with a period of only 3.3 years. When Encke's Comet appeared early in

1941 as a faint fuzzy speck of the seventeenth magnitude it was under observation for the forty-first time. This comet has the shortest period known, but there are many others with periods less than ten years.

Originally comets were known only by the names of the discoverers, such as Lexell's Comet of 1770. But as the periodic comets returned and additional discoverers became numerous this system led to unwieldy combinations—we would identify Encke's Comet by a string of forty-one names. At present the official designation is at first provisional according to the year with a letter to indicate the order of the discovery in that year. After the year is over the provisional listing is revised according to the order in which the comets came to perihelion; thus 1927c, discovered by van Biesbroeck, is now known as 1927 VII. Out of courtesy to the discoverers comets are still often referred to by their names; but not more than three independent discoverers can have their names officially attached to a particular comet. The reason for this limitation is obvious. Recently a bright comet appeared in the morning sky and was discovered by over a score of people; in New Zealand eight men independently discovered it on the same night within a period of five hours.

DISCOVERY

Discovering comets is a great game that anyone can play. At present there is friendly rivalry between amateur and professional astronomers to see who can discover the greater number of new comets. The amateurs use visual telescopes and sweep the sky looking for fuzzy objects that move among the stars. The professional astronomer can seldom spare the time for such sweeps, but relies upon his routine photographic patrol of the sky to record any comets which he may later find when examining the photographs. This technique would seem to give the professional a great advantage, but it has several limitations. Telescopes that can record faint comets take in only small areas of the sky and have little chance of hitting upon a comet while cameras with wide fields usually have small lenses and do not record comets much fainter than the amateur can see. The first comet discovered through photography was found by Barnard in 1892; now more than half the discoveries are made in this way. At present there is a balance between the discoveries by amateurs and professionals, but the scales seem to be tipping in favor of the professional astronomer, for new types of large cameras that cover wide fields are now appearing. Even so the amateur who observes visually still has the advantage of being able to search where he will while the professional examines photographs taken for other purposes in special regions of the sky. The twilight zone which is rarely photographed often contains comets that are near the sun and bright, or have moved up behind the sun in such a manner that we could not see them earlier. Recently two bright comets with tails several degrees long have done this, suddenly appearing near the sun and easily visible to the unaided eye.

The chance that a comet will be discovered depends both upon its brightness and upon how it moves. Some sneak up behind the sun and swing around it in such a manner that they cannot be seen against the bright sky above the sun at twilight. Others passing near the earth may be discovered readily even though much fainter. Our statistics may also be influenced by the return of periodic comets whose positions and motion can be anticipated; they are often relocated while still extremely faint. In Figure 23 we see how bright the comets since 1880 have been at discovery; anticipated comets are not included. For comparison we divide the comets in two groups, those found between 1880 and 1910 and those found between 1910 and 1941. Recently there has been an increase in the number of comets discovered while faint, a result evidently due to the increasing effectiveness of the photographic patrol.

The discovery of a comet is always an exciting event, for we immediately inquire: is it a new comet or an old friend returned after many years; will it become very bright and develop a long tail; will it pass near the earth? We cannot

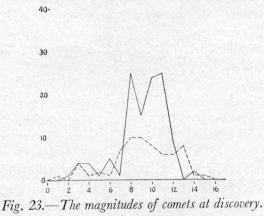

Fig. 23.—The magnitudes of comets at discovery.

The full curve represents the interval 1880 to 1910 and the broken line the interval 1910 to 1941.

answer these questions until we determine the comet's position in space and how it is moving relative to the earth and sun. To do this we require three accurate observations separated by a day or two. Because any particular observatory may be under clouds during this time, astronomers in all parts of the world use a telegraphic code to spread the word of the discovery and the first few observations. The Copenhagen Observatory in Denmark acts as a clearing house for Europe and Asia while the Harvard Observatory acts for the western hemisphere. A typical message reads:

"Comet Okabayasi 04117 October 18490 10073 22513 81101 20153 20056 76503 Hirose Stromgren," which means: "Comet eleventh magnitude with nucleus discovered by Okabayasi. On October 4 (1940) at 18h 49.0m Greenwich Civil Time the position of the comet was right ascension 10h 07m 31.1s, declination $+25°$ 13' 01", moving east 1m 53s, north 0° 56' each day. Message from Hirose (Tokyo), transmitted through Stromgren (Copenhagen)."

Orbit computers who receive such a telegram and then two subsequent observations begin a race to see who can first compute the orbit. To be fair to everyone there are certain rules about the time when work can start. When the hour arrives the computing machines begin to whirl. If all goes well the orbit can be computed and checked in five or six hours, and, to establish priority, is immediately telegraphed to the clearing house. In almost every case the computer assumes a parabolic shape for this preliminary orbit, which will supply a satisfactory time-table of where the comet will be in the sky during the next few weeks. After the comet has finally disappeared and all the observations are collected some computer takes the entire set and derives the accurate definitive orbit.

TYPES OF COMET ORBITS

These orbits generally fall into two rather distinct groups, those that are very nearly parabolic and those that are definitely elliptical and periodic. Just where the dividing line comes depends somewhat upon the accuracy of the observations available to the orbit computer, but the motion of a comet having a period of several hundred years is so nearly that of one moving in a parabola that the periods of these large orbits are very uncertain. Of all new comets discovered since 1900, forty-eight are still represented by parabolic orbits. Of the remaining sixty-three there are thirty-three with eccentricities greater than and thirty with eccentricities less than 0.990.

Of these thirty-three near-parabolic orbits fifteen have eccentricities just slightly greater than one; accordingly we might suppose that they originated in interstellar space. But since the sun moves rapidly through space we should meet some comets head-on at high speed and see them moving in decidedly hyperbolic orbits, yet we find no orbits of this type. Perhaps the hyperbolic orbits we observe are an illusion. When we observe the comets having slightly hyperbolic orbits they are near the sun, well within the orbit of Jupiter and to get there they must move in past the great planets and suffer their perturbations. Careful calculations by Stromgren and others evaluating the planetary attractions affecting more than a dozen of these comets show that when they were at the distance of Neptune from the sun, twenty to thirty years before we observed them, they were all moving in orbits which were ellipses or so slightly hyperbolic that the difference is meaningless. Thus there is no evidence as yet that any comets originate between the stars, but rather that they are all permanent members of the solar system.

Whether or not any of these comets continue to move in hyperbolic orbits and are lost to the solar system has not yet been determined. If a large fraction of them are lost, the number of comets must be diminishing and in the long past the number must have been greater than at present. Should we not care to accept this conclusion, we must find some way by which the supply of comets is continually replenished, some way by which they are continually being formed within the solar system. We cannot satisfactorily consider such possibilities until the next chapter where we discuss what a comet really is.

In Figure 24 we see how the orbits of one hundred parabolic comets are tilted. These far-flung members of the solar system show no regard for the plane in which the planets move, half of them move in the same direction as the planets and half of them move in the opposite direction. Also the majority of them move in planes tilted nearly at right angles to the plane of the planetary motions. According to Figure 25 forty-three per cent of them pass within the earth's orbit and eighty-seven per cent approach the sun within two A.U. We do observe a few that stay far from the sun; they must be

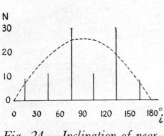

Fig. 24.—*Inclination of near-parabolic comet orbits.*

The dotted line represents a haphazard distribution.

Fig. 25.—*Perihelion distances of near-parabolic comets.*

The majority pass inside or very near the earth's orbit, but some stay well outside.

very great comets representing a multitude of others too faint to be discovered.

We can only guess what intervals these near-parabolic comets require for a trip around the sun. A comet that goes to the distance of the nearest star has a period of the order of a hundred million years and, since the formation of the earth, must have made a score of trips around its vast orbit. If the orbit were much larger, the comet would be pulled away from the solar system by the attraction of some star passing through this part of space. Comets having such great periods may not come near the inner part of the planetary system where we can see them. For all we know there may be a great cometary cloud surrounding the solar system, a vast halo of which we are unaware.

THE PERIODIC COMETS

When we turn from the near-parabolic comets to those with periods less than a hundred years we find increasing signs of organization. Of forty comets observed at more than one apparition only Halley's Comet has an inclination exceeding 90°. All the other periodic comets move in the same direction as the planets and thirty-five of the forty have orbits tilted at less than 45° to the earth's.

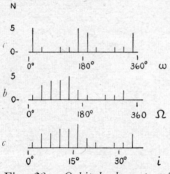

Fig. 26.—*Orbital elements of short-period comets.*

a. Orientation of the long axes. The majority of these comets have their long axes nearly in the plane of the planetary orbits. *b.* Direction of the nodes. The majority of these comets rise across the earth's orbit in the same general direction from the sun. *c.* Inclinations. All are low.

The comets having periodic orbits fall into several groups: those with periods from five to twelve years, thirteen to eighteen years, around twenty-eight years, forty-nine to eighty-one years and longer. When the comets of the first four groups are farthest from the sun their distances are about those of the major planets: Jupiter, Saturn, Uranus and Neptune. Since Jupiter has long been known to have a comet family, each of the other planets was also thought to have a family of comets. Russell showed, however, that because their orbits are appreciably tilted the comets assigned to Saturn, Uranus and Neptune pass closer to massive Jupiter than they do to the planets in whose family they were supposed to be members. The only real family is Jupiter's which includes twenty-four members observed on two or more trips around the sun and nearly as many seen only once.

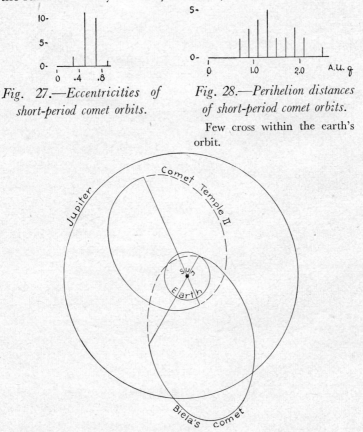

Fig. 27.—*Eccentricities of short-period comet orbits.*

Fig. 28.—*Perihelion distances of short-period comet orbits.*

Few cross within the earth's orbit.

Fig. 29.—*Orbits of Biela's Comet and Comet Temple II.*

Both have orbital inclinations of twelve degrees and require about six years for a trip around the sun.

As Figures 26, 27 and 28 show, . . . the orbits of these comets have low inclinations and are moderately circular. Only five of these short-period comets cross within the earth's orbit, some do not come inside the orbit of Mars. The majority of these comets cross the plane of the earth's orbit in the same general direction from the sun. Since Jupiter crosses this plane 100° around from the Vernal Equinox this is one further indication of the great planet's domination over these comets. One of their most revealing characteristics is the distribution of ω, which measures the angle between the long axis of the orbit and the line where their planes cut through the earth's orbit. The values of ω cluster about 0° and 180° which means that their long axes lie very nearly in the plane of the earth's orbit. When farthest from the sun, these comets are near the distance of Jupiter and about to cross the plane of its orbit. As a result they pass within an astronomical unit of Jupiter every few periods. The resulting perturbations are large and occasionally change the orbit drastically. As an example we choose the orbit of Comet Wolf I which passed within 0.12 A.U. of Jupiter in 1875 and again in

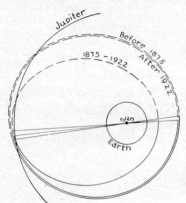

Fig. 30.—Orbits of Comet Wolf I.

The figure shows how this comet moved before it passed near Jupiter in 1875, between 1875 and 1922 and after passing near Jupiter again in 1922. The comet was discovered in 1884 during its second trip around the new orbit. Since 1922 it has remained far from the sun and been extremely faint.

1922. Kamienski of Warsaw thoroughly investigated the changes and found the orbits in Figure 30. The effect of the perturbation of 1875 is most evident in the perihelion distance which decreased and brought the comet near the earth where it was discovered in 1884. Since the perturbation of 1922, which returned the comet to very nearly its original orbit, the comet has passed far from us and has seldom been brighter than the eighteenth magnitude. If we had not discovered it when it had the smaller perihelion distance, we would not know of its existence.

THE CAPTURE PROCESS

The short-period comets are perhaps not so well organized as the asteroids, yet they are unmistakably under the domination of Jupiter. The discussion of how they came to have such orbits leads us farther into how the perturbations of Jupiter effect their motions, gradually reducing their periods until they are completely dominated by the planet. This subservience came about by their being captured from a larger orbit at a time when by chance they passed near the great planet. What type of new orbit the comet will have depends upon the direction and speed at which it approaches Jupiter. If the original orbit was a parabola in the plane of Jupiter's motion, we can find from the following table what type of orbit would result:

TABLE 7

Original Motion		New Orbit
Parallel to Jupiter } Large perihelion		Ellipse, direct motion
Opposite to Jupiter } distance		Hyperbola, direct motion
Toward the sun } Small perihelion		Ellipse, retrograde motion
Away from the sun } distance		Hyperbola, direct motion

We need not worry greatly about the comets thrown into hyperbolic orbits, for they fly away from the solar system and constitute part of the cometary wastage. The most interesting result is for the comets originally moving nearly parallel to Jupiter: they are thrown into orbits of direct motion with short periods. Each time they come near Jupiter, they will again be moving parallel to the planet and will in general have their periods further decreased until

TABLE 8
Number of Comets with Various Periods after Capture from Parabolic Orbits

Periods less than............	6	12	18	24 years
Number..................	126	839	1701	2670

TABLE 9
Size and Shape of Short-period Orbit after Capture

Period after capture, years	Capture from			
	Parabola		Ellipse, Period 130 years	
	$e_{maximum}$	$e_{minimum}$	$e_{maximum}$	$e_{minimum}$
5.20	0.98	0.693	0.95	0.52
5.72	.97	.642	.93	.45
6.28	.96	.596	.91	.38
6.82	.94	.555	.89	.31
7.40	.93	.526	.87	.24

TABLE 10
Some Short-period Comets Discovered Shortly after They Passed near Jupiter

Comet	Near Jupiter	Discovered	Interval, years
Lexell.......................	1767	1770	3
Brorsen.....................	1842	1846	4
Wolf I......................	1875	1884	9
Brooks II...................	1886	1889	3
Faye........................	1841	1843	2
Finlay......................	1862	1886	24
Perrine.....................	1888	1896	8
Swift.......................	1886	1895	9
Whipple....................	1922	1933	11

they are firmly captured in Jupiter's family. Those comets thrown into retrograde ellipses meet Jupiter head-on at the next close-approach and are likely to be expelled from the solar system. Once this selective process has been operating

TABLE 11

EFFECTS OF THE CAPTURE PROCESS

Comet	Time	Semi-major axis	Peri-helion distance	Period, years
Lexell	Before 1767	5.06	2.96	11.4
	1770	3.15	0.67	5.6
	After 1779	6.37	3.33	16.2
Brooks II	Before 1886	9.0	5.44	27.0
	1889–1921	3.59	1.95	6.8
	After 1921	3.64	1.86	6.95 (the orientation of the orbit was completely reversed in 1921)
Wolf I	Before 1875	4.18	2.54	8.54
	1875–1922	3.59	1.59	6.80
	After 1922	4.07	2.36	8.20
Coma Sola	Before 1912	4.46	2.15	9.43
	After 1912	4.17	1.77	8.52
Schwassmann-Wachmann II	Before 1921	4.43	3.55	9.30
	After 1921	3.46	2.09	6.42

for a few million years we find the comets of short-period moving in direct orbits of low inclination.

The rate at which Jupiter's family grows depends greatly upon how the comets move before being captured. If they

move in parabolas turned at all angles to the planet's
motion, Jupiter must change their motions greatly and can
capture only a few that pass very near. H. A. Newton concluded that of every thousand million comets crossing Jupiter's orbit in parabolas the numbers thrown into orbits of
short-period would be those in Table 8. Three-fourths of the
839 comets taking on periods less than twelve years will
have direct motions, most of them at small inclinations.
Since there are many short-period comets, we might conclude that myriads of comets moving in parabolas must be
crossing Jupiter's orbit. But we cannot take the figures in
Table 8 too literally.

In their studies of this capture process the great French
mathematicians Tisserand and Callandreau found that the
difference between motion originally in a parabola and in a
large ellipse allows a great diversity in the shape of the final
orbit, Table 9. Most of the short-period comets undoubtedly
come to their present orbits from ones of only slightly longer
periods and the production of short-period orbits proceeds
in many steps each involving only a small change.

CHANGING ORBITS

Among the periodic comets, especially those of short-
period, we find a continual state of change. Some move in
past the earth for a few revolutions only to be whisked back
into orbits that keep them far from the sun and unobserva-
ble. In Table 10 we see that many of the short-period comets
were first observed only one or two periods after they passed
Jupiter and had their orbits severely altered. Table 11 contains the former orbits of a few comets; before they approached Jupiter closely they moved with moderate periods
and such large perihelion distances that we could not discover them. To trace back the orbits of all short-period

comets would be a laborious task, but undoubtedly they would exhibit large variations.

In addition to such large sudden changes the orbits of some comets show small progressive changes; Comet Pons-Winnecke is a good example. This comet was first discovered by Pons in 1819, but not observed again for forty years until in 1858 Winnecke rediscovered it. Since then it has been observed nearly every time it passed the sun at intervals of six years. Table 12 includes a sufficient number

TABLE 12
ORBITS OF COMET PONS-WINNECKE

	1819 III	*1858 II*	*1886 VI*	*1898 II*	*1927 VII*	*1933 II*
ω	162°	162°	172°	173°	170°	169°
Ω	113°	113°	104°	101°	98°	97°
i	10°.7	10°.8	14°.5	17°.0	18°.9	20°.1
q^*	0.774	0.764	0.886	0.924	1.04	1.10 A.U.
e	0.755	0.755	0.726	0.715	0.685	0.672
P	5.62	5.56	5.80	5.88	5.99	6.16 years

* q *is the perihelion distance.*

of orbits to show the gradual progressive changes that have occurred. Note how the tilt of the orbit has doubled, how the position at which it cuts the earth's orbit has moved around, and especially how the distance of closest approach to the sun has increased from 0.77 A.U., near the orbit of Venus, to 1.10 A.U. well outside the earth's orbit. If by chance the comet had not been observed from 1819 to 1933, we would not identify 1933 I with 1819 III, but would consider them as two distinct comets and Comet 1819 III would be listed as "lost."

While Comet Pons-Winnecke was undergoing these large orbital variations its motion was nearly in resonance with

Jupiter's, the comet making two revolutions to one of Jupiter's. In Figure 7 we found few asteroids having such resonant motion and the rapid changes of this comet's orbit illustrate the manner in which an asteroid taking on resonant motion is speedily shifted into a different orbit. Changes of this sort are of such a size that we cannot keep account of the comet unless it is observed frequently. If it sneaks around behind the sun and misses being observed at several consecutive perihelion passages we may have difficulty in predicting where to search when it is next due near the earth. Looking for a needle in a haystack is simple compared to locating a faint comet whose position is unknown.

Vanishing Comets

A sizable number of periodic comets have been observed only once or twice and then not found again when subsequently due at perihelion. In some cases the predicted positions were too inaccurate to be dependable, at other times little attempt was made to locate the comet because other endeavors distracted the observers. Yet in a few cases careful observations were made according to a reliable timetable, but no comet found. We are always hampered by the gradual fading of the short-period comets sometimes amounting to nearly a magnitude in a century. But in addition to this gradual wasting away, some comets have disintegrated while under observation. Although the process is disastrous to the comet, it makes the comet famous and simultaneously tells us much about its structure.

The most notable example of such disintegration is Biela's Comet, first observed in 1772. It was observed again in 1815 and 1826 when its periodic orbit was derived. Thereafter it appeared on schedule in 1832, but in 1839 it stayed near the sun in the sky and was not located. In 1845 after an absence of thirteen years it appeared much as it had before. In the middle of January 1846 several observers were astonished to find two comets where one had been a few nights previously. These two comets moved along together changing in brightness in a singular manner, first one then the other being the brighter. Calculating back the relative positions of the two components Hubbard found that the comet probably split more than a year before it was observed as double, but by chance one component was hidden behind the other until they were near the earth.

Naturally the return of this double comet in 1852 was eagerly awaited. It came on schedule and had only one peculiarity—one component was bright and the other faint. In 1859, as in 1839, it was nearly in line with the sun and passed unobserved, but in 1865 should again have been favorably placed for observation. But it could not be found and has never been seen since. The general loosening up that developed between 1832 and 1845 probably continued and the comet became too scattered and faint to be visible. We have more evidence about what happened to Biela's Comet, but that comes in Chapter 7 where we discuss meteor showers.

Evidently comets are not solid bodies, but can break up to such an extent that they are no longer observable. When a comet passes near some massive body, like the sun or Jupiter, the body pulls on the comet with a disrupting force that varies with the distance between them. Thus the near side of the comet will be pulled away from the far side unless it contains enough material to hold itself together. Mathematical astronomers find that the density necessary for a swarm of particles or a cloud of gas to remain intact under the attraction of a massive body, is three times the density that the attracting body would have if it were uniformly spread out over a volume whose radius is the distance

between it and the comet. When a comet's density drops
below the critical value, which changes rapidly with the
distance between the comet and the sun or planet, the
comet is pulled apart.

A comet stable at a certain distance from the sun at one
time will not necessarily be stable when it passes again. A
wide variety of mechanisms operate to disperse the matter
of the comet, thereby lowering its density and ability to
hold together. A list of these mechanisms includes:

Continual loss of material into the tail,

Collisions between the particles composing the comet and
other particles moving between the planets,

Electrical repulsion between particles resulting from
charges built up by photoelectric action of sunlight and
cosmic rays,

The Poynting-Robertson effect which sorts out the large
and small particles into different orbits.

This multiplicity of disintegrating forces is counterbalanced
so far as we know only by the gravitational attractions
between the particles which are at best small forces. In
Table 13 we find the distances from the various planets at
which the solar and planetary forces are equal, the minimum stable density at that position, and the distances from
the planets at which they are as effective in destroying
comets as the sun is at one astronomical unit. We observe
few comets which do not come within the orbit of Mars
where the minimum stable density is one hundred millionth
of a gram per cubic centimeter—about one ten thousandth
that of air at sea level. This seems very little, but a swarm
of stony particles the size of water drops separated by only a
meter has approximately this average density.

From Table 13 we notice that a comet which is stable
under the sun's attraction when crossing the orbit of Mars
will be pulled apart by Jupiter only when it approaches very

TABLE 13
The Disruptive Forces of the Planets

Planet	Solar distance	Planetary distance for force equal sun's, A.U.	Limiting* density, gm. per cc.	Planetary distance for force equal sun's at 1 A.U.
Mercury........	0.39	0.0019	7.4×10^{-6}	0.0048
Venus.........	0.72	0.0098	1.1×10^{-6}	.013
Earth.........	1.00	0.0144	4.3×10^{-7}	.014
Mars..........	1.52	0.011	1.2×10^{-7}	.0067
Jupiter........	5.20	0.51	3.0×10^{-9}	.096
Saturn.........	9.54	0.63	5.0×10^{-10}	.064
Uranus........	19.2	0.68	6.2×10^{-11}	.034
Neptune.......	30.0	1.11	1.6×10^{-11}	.036
Pluto..........	39.5	0.53	7.0×10^{-12}	.013

*7.4×10^{-6} is equivalent to 0.000,007,4.

close to that planet. The pull of the sun, not that of Jupiter, causes comets to disintegrate. Of course Jupiter may hasten the end by thinning out the cometary material when the comet passes near. This is probably what happened with Biela's Comet which split after it had been near Jupiter in 1842 and was again moving towards the sun. Similarly Taylor's Comet, which divided in 1916 and was never seen again, split in two when it was nearest the sun.

This general picture of how a comet may go to pieces is supported by the behavior of Ensor's Comet, 1926 III, which had a parabolic orbit. The comet was of the eighth magnitude when discovered two months before it reached perihelion at 0.33 A.U. and, according to the normal behavior of comets, it should have become easily visible to the unaided eye. Instead as it neared perihelion it spread out, became very diffuse, faded rapidly and soon disappeared. Comet Westphal having a period of sixty-one years behaved similarly in 1913. As it moved toward perihelion at 1.25 A.U. it became very diffuse and faded by ten magnitudes in six weeks. These comets dispersed and disappeared because they were not dense enough to withstand the sun's disruptive forces.

One comet whose existence is difficult to explain is Comet Brooks II. In 1886 it passed very close to Jupiter, going between the satellites and nearly grazing the surface of the planet. At such a small distance, we should expect the great planet to have torn the comet to shreds. Despite this close approach to Jupiter the comet is still intact and was last observed in 1939. It has, however, been fading as though it were loosening up and it may disintegrate and disappear within the next few decades.

5

ANATOMY OF A COMET

A BRIGHT COMET APPEARS AS A FUZZY SPOT IN THE SKY
with a tail stretching out like a plume of smoke. As it moves
inside the earth's orbit to perihelion and starts its journey
out into cold interplanetary space the comet rapidly goes
through a variety of changes, increasing in brightness,
growing a tail, and sometimes showing remarkable variations of structure within a few hours. No two comets behave
exactly alike and even those that return periodically rarely
behave alike at successive appearances. Such changes tell us
immediately that comets are unique among the population
of the solar system, for they are not solid bodies but great
clouds of gas surrounding small clusters of particles.

Through a telescope we see the head of a comet as two
distinct parts: a small sharp nucleus embedded in a large
nebulous coma. As we focus our attention upon the nucleus
and examine it under higher and higher magnification its
size does not increase—it always looks like a star seen
through a fog. Perhaps there is no real nucleus in the comet,
but just a sharp increase in brightness which we see as a central point of light. Indeed some comets have been without a
visible nucleus, merely appearing as a large nebulous patch
of light.

Fig. 31.—Comet Cunningham, 1940c, photographed on Christmas Eve, 1940.

This comet was remarkable for its very narrow, ribbon-like tail.

The coma of a comet is a large luminous envelope, brightest around the nucleus and gradually fading off until it can no longer be seen. Within the coma of a few comets, usually the brightest and most active, are sharp gradations of light surrounding the nucleus. These envelopes expand through

Fig. 32.—Halley's Comet, May 5, 1910.

Here the bright star-like nucleus is seen imbedded within the diffuse coma. (*Lick Observatory.*)

the coma like a series of waves, eventually vanishing. The heads of comets are usually tens of thousands of kilometers across, rivalling the size of Jupiter; a few have even exceeded the size of the sun.

Comet tails generally point away from the sun. As a comet moves toward the sun the tail trails behind; as it moves

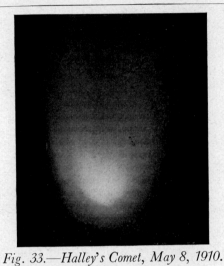

Fig. 33.—Halley's Comet, May 8, 1910.

Several envelopes or sharp gradations of light within the coma are
visible. (*Lick Observatory.*)

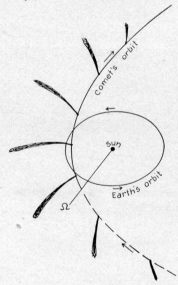

Fig. 34.—A comet's tail points away from the sun.

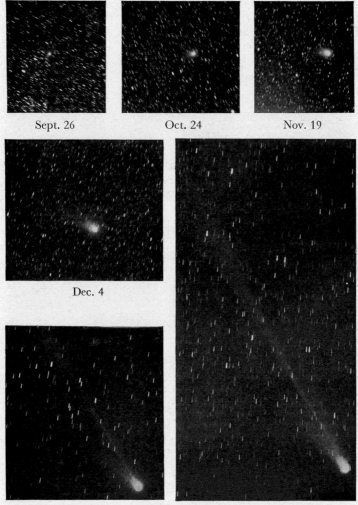

Sept. 26   Oct. 24   Nov. 19

Dec. 4

Dec. 18   Dec. 25

Fig. 35.—The development of Cunningham's Comet, 1940c.

When first discovered the comet was very small and faint. Near the first of December it began to develop a real tail and ceased to look like a polly-wog. These six photographs are all on the same scale and had the same exposure times.

away from the sun it goes tail first. The tail then suggests the beam from a flashlight illuminating the path the comet will travel. Those of us who marvel at the beauty of a great comet's tail stretching across the sky are fortunate to live on the earth and not on Jupiter or one of the other planets at the outskirts of the solar system, for comets very rarely grow their tails until they have passed inside the orbit of Mars. At greater distances from the sun a comet is all coma, a pollywog with a stubby tail a few hundred thousand kilometers long. In a typical case the real tail does not begin to grow until the comet is about to cross the earth's orbit. Then the activity begins and the tail shoots out at the rate of a million kilometers per day until it may be fifty to a hundred million kilometers long. The maximum tail length on record is that of the great comet of 1843; its tail stretched three hundred million kilometers into space, twice the distance from the earth to the sun. In 1910 the tail of Halley's Comet grew to fifty million kilometers by the time it passed perihelion, and continued to grow for several weeks thereafter, reaching a maximum length of one hundred and fifty million kilometers. The apparent length of such a tail depends upon the angle at which we see it. When in 1910 the earth passed probably through the tail of Halley's Comet it stretched 150°, nearly across the entire sky. Although a few weeks later the tail was actually longer, it then appeared to us only one-third as great.

FORMATION OF COMET TAILS

As we see a comet's tail in the sky it always points away from the sun and must actually extend away from the sun, like a plume of smoke floating down wind. Some force emanating from the sun was long recognized as the cause but the force was not identified until the beginning of this century when physicists showed that light exerts a pressure on tiny particles and actually does blow them away. This outward force is extremely small and effects only minute dust particles and molecules of gas. As it pushes on these

Fig. 36.—Comet 1910 I.

The tail of this bright comet consisted of several curved parts. (*Lowell Observatory.*)

bits of matter, it counteracts or dilutes the gravitational attraction of the sun. When a comet nears the sun the amount of sunlight passing through it increases at exactly the same rate as the pull of the sun increases, so the net result of the attraction and repulsion does not change.

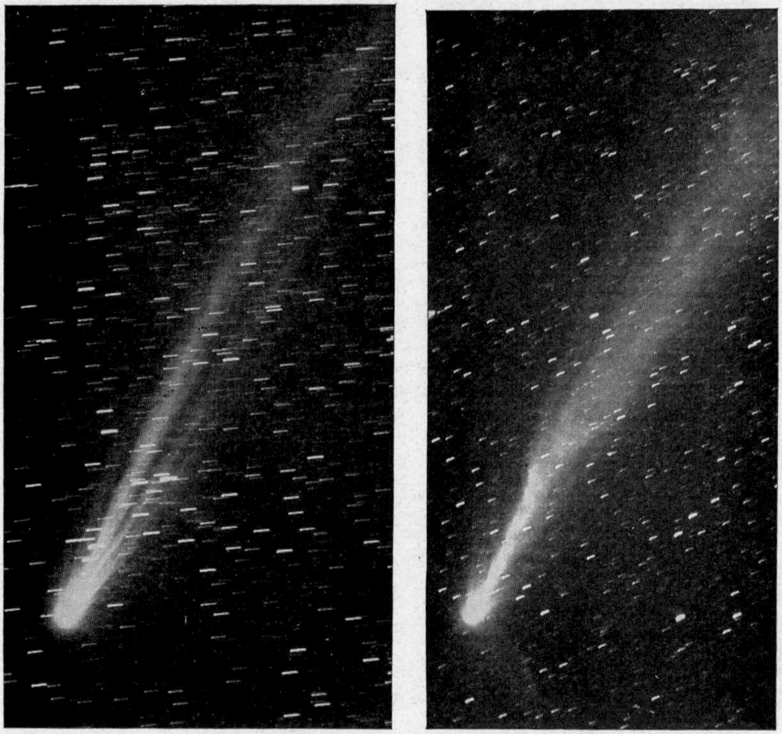

a   b

Fig. 37.—Variations in Comet Morehouse.

a. The comet on October 23, 1908. *b.* A week later, October 30, 1908.

If a comet moved directly toward the sun, its tail would point radially outward, but comets move around the sun and this motion spreads their tails over curved paths. When the material rushes out at a tremendous rate, the tail appears almost straight; but when it floats away leisurely, the tail is decidedly curved. Often a comet has several tails of different curvature showing at the same time as did Comet 1910 I, Figure 36.

When a tail contains small knots or irregularities we can identify them on successive days and measure their rate of motion thereby evaluating the forces propelling them away from the sun. Usually the outward force is only a few times greater than the sun's attraction, but Eddington and

Fig. 38.—Rapid changes in Comet Morehouse.

On October 15, 1908 a great cloud of gas shot out along the comet's tail. On the preceding night the comet showed no indications that this great outburst was about to occur. (*Yerkes Observatory.*)

Cherrington found forces more than a thousand times greater than gravitation acting upon Comet Morehouse, 1908 III. This comet was one of the most active ever seen. Within a few days it radically changed its appearance and often showed great clouds or jets of material moving millions of kilometers along the tail in only a few hours.

All the material in a comet's tail is moving in hyperbolic orbits and is lost to the comet. Obviously no comet can keep producing a limitless number of tails, even though each contains only a small quantity of material. We are not surprised to find that the comets of short-period that come within the earth's orbit now grow no appreciable appendages. Their supply of tail-stuff has been exhausted during their many past trips around the sun. Halley's Comet continues to grow elegant tails after thirty observed trips around the sun, but even it seems to have faded by two magnitudes in the past thousand years.

A Comet's Brightness

As comets approach the sun they brighten rapidly, but at various rates. Consequently we have difficulties in predicting how bright any particular comet will become when nearest the sun. An asteroid that reflects sunlight brightens according to the amount of sunlight falling on it, but comets brighten more rapidly. For comparison, an asteroid will become four times brighter by halving its solar distance, but a typical comet will become sixteen times brighter and some comets even become fifty times more luminous.

Comet Cunningham well illustrates the difficulty of making these predictions of brightness. When discovered in September 1940 the comet was of the thirteenth magnitude and half way out to Jupiter's orbit. Since at perihelion it would pass within the orbit of Mercury, the comet was obviously due to brighten greatly. The most optimistic predictions made it very bright while all estimates showed that it would be visible to the unaided eye. Until early December the comet brightened according to the more optimistic predictions, but then the rate decreased and when brightest the comet was just a faint hazy spot comparable to the Andromeda Nebula.

Vsessviatsky has attempted to intercompare the intrinsic brightness of comets by computing for them absolute magnitudes—how bright they would be at one astronomical unit from the sun and earth. In Figure 39 we find the absolute magnitudes he derived for some near-parabolic comets and notice that they have a great diversity. The short-period comets are among the faintest known, generally having absolute magnitudes between eight and fourteen. Vsessviatsky and Bobrovnikoff have concluded

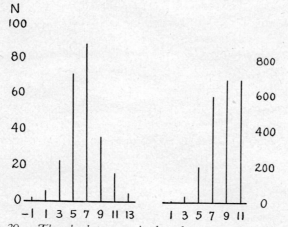

Fig. 39.—The absolute magnitudes of near-parabolic comets.

To the left is the observed distribution, to the right the true distribution, according to Bourgeois and Cox, in which faint comets are extremely abundant.

that the short-period comets are fading rapidly and cannot survive many hundreds of trips around the sun. Yet we shall find evidence that Encke's Comet has been moving in essentially its present orbit for perhaps ten thousand years, during which time it has made a total of several thousand approaches within 0.4 A.U. of the sun. Although one of the faintest comets known, it is still visible.

Perhaps the greatest comet ever observed was that of 1729 which never approached within four astronomical units of the sun yet was visible to the unaided eye. At the same solar distance Halley's Comet was ten magnitudes fainter. This great comet of 1729 had an absolute magnitude near −6, completely outside the limits of Figure 39. The fact that it could be observed with the unaided eye at that great solar distance while many other comets passing near the earth can barely be seen through large telescopes emphasizes our difficulties in discovering and properly counting the intrinsically faint comets. Bourgeois and Cox have computed what chances we have to discover comets of various absolute magnitudes and they conclude that the actual distribution of absolute magnitudes is that of the right-hand curve in Figure 39. Even this distribution is provisional, but it clearly shows that among the comets as well as the asteroids we are merely skimming the bright objects from the total. How many comets belong to the solar system we can only guess for we have no idea how many come to perihelion at the distance of Jupiter, Saturn, and Uranus, or how many have extremely long period orbits bringing them among the planets at tremendous intervals. Yet any reasonable guess must make the total, bright and faint, among the hundreds of thousands.

Some of the difficulties we have in predicting the brightness of comets are well illustrated by the behavior of Comet Holmes and Comet Schwassmann-Wachmann I. On November 6, 1892, Holmes discovered a comet faintly visible to the unaided eye. According to its orbit the comet should have been bright and well placed for discovery throughout the previous two months yet it had escaped detection. In January 1893, after two weeks of cloudy weather, Barnard hoped to have one last look at it before it faded beyond the limit of his telescope. Instead of a very faint fuzzy area, he found it bright, appearing as a star of the eighth magnitude. During successive nights it increased in size, regaining an appearance similar to that at its discovery. Presumably it had been faint when nearest the sun, then flared up and was immediately found. In 1899 it was again visible to the unaided eye, but in 1906 was very faint. Since then it has not been seen.

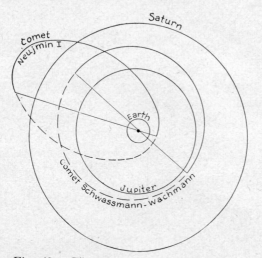

Fig. 40.—The orbits of two periodic comets.

Comet Schwassmann-Wachmann has an extremely circular orbit which keeps the comet between the orbits of Jupiter and Saturn. Comet Neujmin I is more typical of the periodic comets we know. Their orbital inclinations are respectively 9° and 15°; both have periods near 17 years.

Comet Schwassmann-Wachmann I has the most peculiar orbit known, for it has an eccentricity of only 0.142 and an average distance of 6.43 A.U. from the sun. As a result the comet remains in the region between Jupiter and Saturn, coming to perihelion at 5.51 A.U. and to aphelion at 7.34 A.U. Generally it is near the eighteenth magnitude and would have passed unknown except for its peculiar ability to flare up suddenly, becoming a hundred times brighter within a few days. Such flares have occurred several times. The comet brightens very quickly, in 1934 on March 10 it was of the eighteenth and on March 14 of the thirteenth magnitude. Within a few weeks it faded away to its original brightness. We do not know what kind of light it gives off when bright, but something drastic must happen. One possible explanation suggests that the comet intercepts a great burst of ultra-violet light from a hot-spot on the sun, becomes wildly excited and then fades back to normal. Such a theory would seem more reasonable if other comets behaved similarly, but few give signs of such abrupt disturbances.

The total quantity of matter in a comet cannot be measured accurately, for they have too little mass to exert any measurable pull upon any planet they approach. Lexell's Comet passed so close to the earth in 1770 that our meager pull changed its period by several days, yet no observable changes in the motion or rotation of the earth resulted. This comet must have had a mass less than a ten thousandth that of the earth. Yet this would be a sizable amount of material, nearly a million million million tons. The real mass of even a great comet is, however, probably much below this value, possibly only a million million tons.

When we spread this amount of material over a space the volume of Jupiter, there is very little per cubic kilometer. What we observe as a beautiful comet sweeping across the sky was described by Percival Lowell as "a bag-full of nothing." The amount of material within a thousand cubic kilometers of a comet's tail is less than that in a cubic centimeter of ordinary air. One favorite form of speculation is what would happen to the earth if we collided with a comet or its tail. If we only hit the tail, as we probably did in 1861 and 1910, nothing unusual would happen, the sky might be a trifle brighter than usual because we would be looking into the bright stuff of the comet's tail. If the earth

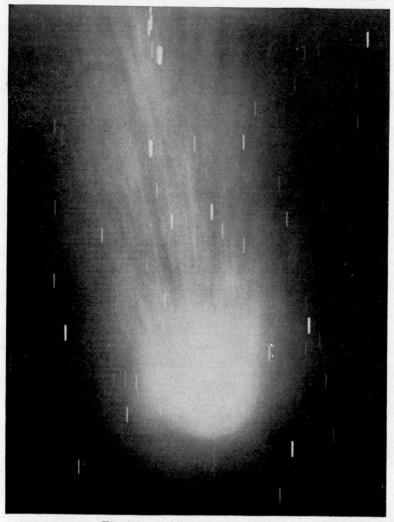

Fig. 41.—"A bag-full of nothing."

Halley's Comet June 2, 1910. Photographed at the Mount Wilson
Observatory through the 60-inch telescope.

met the nucleus of the comet, which probably contains the greater part of all the comet's mass, we might see a very intense meteor shower, but probably nothing more serious would result.

THE LIGHT OF COMETS

If we photograph the light of a comet after dispersing it through a prism, the resulting spectrum differs greatly

Fig. 42.—The spectrum of Comet Cunningham.

The light of the comet was passed through a glass prism and photographed on a film sensitive to all radiations from violet to red. At various colors separate images of the comet appear. That on the left is caused by violet light from cyanogen, while those in the center are blue-green and greenish from carbon molecules. No strong images appear in the yellow and red light at the right. The band of light down the center is probably reflected sunlight.

from that of the asteroids. Down the center of the image, where the bright nucleus of the comet lies, is a continuous band of color from the red to the violet. So far as we can tell this is principally sunlight reflected from small solid particles and dust within the nucleus. At various places along this band of color are small images of the comet, each distinctly separate. Some are large and some are small, each tells its own story about the comet.

Before we can properly interpret these separate images, we should photograph the comet through another more

complicated spectrograph which contains a narrow slit.
With a large telescope we concentrate the light of the comet
upon this slit behind which are prisms to disperse the colors
and a camera to record them for us. The photograph we
obtain consists of many little images of the slit, each photographed in different colors. The nucleus again gives us a
faint continuous band of color, but the separate images of
the comet now appear as narrow lines, or close groups of
lines whose positions along the spectrum can be measured
very accurately. For an explanation of this result we turn
to the physics laboratory and find that only atoms of hot
gases give off such patterns of isolated lines, and that gas

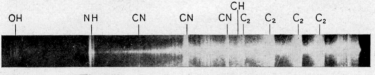

OH   NH   CN   CN   CN CH C_2 C_2 C_2 C_2

Fig. 43.—Details of a comet's spectrum.

The light of Comet Cunningham photographed through a slit spectrograph to show in detail the radiations of various molecules. The presence
of OH and NH in a comet was discovered from this photograph by Elvey,
Swings and Babcock. (*McDonald Observatory.*)

molecules give off close groups of lines. By testing various
types of gases and carefully noting where their light comes
along the spectrum, we can identify most of the strong lines
in the cometary spectra with gases containing carbon, C;
hydrogen, H; oxygen, O; and nitrogen, N. So far the molecules identified are carbon, C_2; cyanogen, CN; methyne,
CH; carbon monoxide, CO; nitrogen, N_2; nitrogen
hydride, NH and hydroxyl, OH. The latter two have
been found by Elvey, Swings and Babcock in the deep
ultra-violet spectrum of Comet Cunningham. Several of
these gases are poisonous but since each molecule is separated from its nearest companion by several miles, we have
nothing to fear from passing through a comet's tail.

When far from the sun the principal radiation of a comet comes from CN, but as the comet approaches the sun the light of C_2 and CH increases in intensity. Within the orbit of Mars the patterns of CO and N_2 appear, principally in the budding tail. Comets that venture well within the earth's orbit show other progressive spectral changes, some of the radiations fade rapidly while others brighten. Near the distance of Venus from the sun the yellow light of sodium appears and dominates the spectrum of a comet closely approaching the sun. The great comet of 1882 II passed within five hundred thousand kilometers of the sun where the solid materials within the nucleus must have been heated to 3000°C. The spectrum of this comet contained seventeen bright lines due to the atoms of sodium and iron, and possibly of chromium and nickel. Since the light of a comet comes from such a mixture of molecules and atoms, each of which changes in brightness with distance from the sun, we do well to predict with any accuracy how the brightness of a comet will increase as it approaches the sun.

The failure of Comet Cunningham to continue brightening seems attributable to the delayed appearance of bright yellow sodium radiation. Normally it should have appeared near mid-December, but did not show up until just before the New Year when the comet was only 0.6 A.U. from the sun.

A comet is not a self-luminous body, but shines by sunlight which is both reflected by the solid particles and is absorbed and reemitted by the gas molecules. These molecules are very greedy and can take up large quantities of deep violet light from the sun and turn it into the colors we can see and photograph. In the process some of the molecules are broken apart and no longer give off light. As a comet moves toward perihelion and the intensity of sunlight increases, more and more molecules break apart until at very small solar distances few exist and we see only the radiations from the separated atoms evaporated from the solid materials of the nucleus. Wurm investigated how sunlight disrupts the molecules in comets and found that the molecules of CO and N_2 broke up less easily than those of C_2, CH and CN. These latter molecules, when freed within the coma of a comet, are soon torn apart and disappear. The longer lived molecules of CO and N_2 hold together and are blown out into the comet's tail where they are the sole visible constituents. As the comet nears the sun these molecules are broken more rapidly and the apparent size of the coma decreases. This was apparent with Halley's Comet in 1910 which shrank from a diam-eter of 230,000 kilometers to 40,000 kilometers when near the sun.

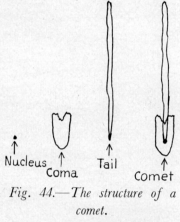

Fig. 44.—The structure of a comet.

The light of a comet comes from three different sources; the nucleus reflects sunlight, the coma emits light from short-lived molecules, while the tail emits light from less-fragile molecules.

The short-period comets have three characteristics which are all signs of old age: they do not grow tails, they are intrinsicly faint and their spectra show only a few faint gase-ous radiations superimposed upon a reflection-spectrum. We have little idea how long these comets may have been members of Jupiter's family or how many times in the past they have moved in near the sun, each time suffering further depletion of their gas supply.

Not only does a comet continually lose material into its tail, but several great comets have developed satellitic

comets which ran along with them for a few days or weeks
before fading from view. One clue to this phenomenon is
given by the comet of 1882. When it passed closest to the
sun its nucleus seemed to break into four or more separate
parts, like beads on a string. Simultaneously at least one
satellitic comet appeared. In 1880 another bright comet
had moved in nearly the same orbit and in 1887 a third
one moving similarly appeared. We call this concurrence
a comet group and wonder if they were not originally one
great comet which split when it passed close to the sun at
some previous perihelion passage. The disruptive force of
the sun at the small perihelion distance of these comets
must be terrific and it is surprising that any parts of them
could survive a first perihelion passage to return even as
fragments at a later time.

We have never observed any sizable body within the
nucleus of a comet. In 1910 Halley's Comet passed between
the earth and sun, yet not the slightest shadow of the comet
could be seen against the sun's disk; a solid body fifty kilometers across would have appeared as a small dot moving
across the sun. Comet Pons-Winnecke came very close to
the earth in 1927 and allowed us to examine its internal
structure. Both Baldet and Slipher examined the nucleus
under high magnification and concluded that any solid
mass there could not be more than one or two kilometers
across. Indeed, from its brightness Baldet found the nucleus
could not be a solid body larger than 400 meters in diameter. Since comets disintegrate into meteor streams we
visualize the head of a comet as a swarm of solid particles
crowded together to form the nucleus and gradually
thinning out toward the edge of the coma. Surrounding
them are quantities of various gases, some that we can
observe and probably some we cannot, which move along
with the particles or escape from them under the stimula-

tion of the sun's light. As time passes the comet loses material into its tail, gradually becomes spread out, may have its nucleus depleted of solid material and eventually it can hold together no longer. Then it quickly breaks up and vanishes; the debris continues to move along in much the same orbit awaiting a collision with the earth to reveal its presence as a meteor shower.

THE ORIGIN OF COMETS

The origin of the great clusters of particles dodging in and out among the planets is one of the most difficult problems we have to solve about the solar system. Many suggestions of how they could have come into existence have been put forward and we shall review them briefly although not one is satisfactory, for they all run counter to some part of our meager knowledge of what a comet is.

We might say that comets represent the debris left over when the solar system was formed. But that is no answer for we do not know how the solar system was formed. Furthermore comets consist of small clusters of stony particles which if widely scattered in space would have no tendency to draw together. They move in orbits tilted at all angles while the planets move in circular orbits all in the same plane.

We might say that comets were not originally part of the solar system, that they disintegrate too rapidly to have lasted two billion years. In that case they must be of recent origin. One suggestion has them captured by the sun when it moved through some great cloud of dust particles drifting between the stars, perhaps the Orion Nebula. If that were the case, only comets moving in certain directions could be captured and the present arrangement of the long-period and parabolic orbits should show some trace of the preferential direction, yet they come from all directions of space with equal abundance. Such an origin by capture places the responsibility for creating comets upon some indefinable process transpiring in the depths of space. We should consider skeptically whether clusters as dense as comets could form from scattered particles moving between the stars.

Perhaps the comets are constantly being formed within the solar system. Since we continually find new comets appearing shortly after they passed close to Jupiter, they may be shot out of volcanoes of Jupiter and Saturn like the pellets from a shot-gun. Such a scheme leads immediately to difficulties; we do not know that there are volcanoes on Jupiter or Saturn. Furthermore these great planets are loath to let any material escape from them; the particles would have to have high initial velocities to get free. If the particles were initially moving fast enough to escape, they would probably be consumed as meteors while penetrating the thick atmosphere encasing the planet. Should we grant the possibility of overcoming all these objections, we still have to account in some other way for the long-period and parabolic comets.

We might say that comets formed from material shot from the sun in the form of great solar prominences. But such material moving out from the sun must fall back into it, not come to perihelion at distances of several hundred million kilometers. As a last possibility we might consider the collision of two asteroids. Since they are all moving in the same direction they would not hit very hard, but even so they might break up into splinters. Yet we have difficulty in visualizing how such a collision could result in the formation of the closely-knit organization of particles that constitute a comet.

Perhaps we should be very honest and say that we do now know how, when or where comets were formed.

6

SHOOTING-STARS

DAILY BILLIONS OF TINY PARTICLES DASH INTO THE earth's atmosphere, flare for a moment and disappear. These brief streaks of light are meteors, popularly known as shooting-stars. For many centuries they were thought to be some local phenomenon, like lightning flashes, hence the term meteor—meaning something in the atmosphere. No scientific attempt to determine what meteors were was made until the end of the eighteenth century. In 1798 two German students, Brandes and Benzenberg, noticed that although they were several kilometers apart they saw the same meteors, but in different parts of the sky. They realized that the meteors could not be some nearby phenomenon, like lightning flashes; neither could they be at enormous distances like the moon and planets. After carefully observing the paths of numerous meteors, they were able to compute the heights and positions of some by the simple process of triangulation, just as a surveyor locates a distant inaccessible mountain, Figure 46. To visualize the effect, hold a finger at arm's length and notice how its position against the distant background changes when viewed alternately with the left and right eye. From their first observations

Fig. 45.—A brilliant fireball.

Brandes and Benzenberg found that meteors flame high above the earth at altitudes around eighty kilometers. A few rough estimates of how many seconds the meteors were visible showed that they had velocities of at least several kilometers a second and must have come from the parts of space beyond the moon.

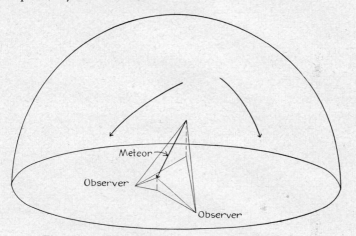

Fig. 46.—The real and apparent path of a meteor.

How a meteor plunging through the atmosphere appears to two widely separated observers.

These results received little attention for over thirty years. On November 12, 1833, however, a great meteor shower, so rich that the meteors were as thick as snowflakes, once again attracted attention to these celestial rockets. Several persons independently noticed that the meteors of the shower spread out from a point in the constellation Leo much as the ribs of an umbrella spread out from the point. To interpret this effect we need only notice how the parallel sides of a long room seem to converge in the distance. If we trace the meteor paths backward they too converge in the distance at a point we call their radiant.

TABLE 14
CHARACTERISTICS OF METEOR SHOWERS

Shower	Date of maximum	Radiant		Velocity, km./sec.
		R.A.	Dec.	
Quadrantids.............	January 3	232°	52°	46
Lyrids..................	April 21	280°	37	51
Eta Aquarids............	May 4	336°	−1	66
Delta Aquarids..........	July 28	340°	−17	50
Perseids................	August 12	47°	57	61
Orionids................	October 22	96°	15	68
Leonids.................	November 16	152°	22	72
Geminids...............	December 12	110°	33	36

This effect of perspective can mean only one thing: the meteors of the shower moved in parallel orbits before they hit the earth and must constitute a great stream of bodies moving around the sun. This discovery established the astronomical significance of meteors as the minutia of the solar system worthy of extensive study.

OBSERVING METEORS

During the past century many other showers have been discovered. Table 14 summarizes some of the characteristics of the most conspicuous showers which are identified by the constellations from which they radiate. But not all meteors come from recognized showers; some are sporadic and provide a background against which the shower meteors appear.

Unfortunately a meteor gives no warning of its impending dash into the atmosphere. Suddenly it flames across the sky and abruptly disappears. What it is and whence it came must be determined from the observations secured in those few seconds that cannot be anticipated. When we go meteor-observing we must take pot-luck. Professional astronomers have no better fortune than amateurs and the study of meteors is one field of astronomy in which amateurs, working according to pre-arranged schedules and programs, aid the professional astronomer to achieve the fabulous condition of being in several places at once. The American Meteor Society,* which consists principally of amateurs working under the direction of Olivier, has collected vast quantities of information about meteors. In Canada several groups of amateur observers assist Millman in the photography of meteor trails and spectra.

Meteors differ greatly in brightness. Some are so brilliant they flood-light several states as they blaze to oblivion; a few appear even in daylight. These brightest meteors are generally termed fireballs, but how bright they must be to warrant this special designation is a matter of choice. One astronomer adopted a very practical definition: "A fireball is a meteor sufficiently bright to make people report it." The great majority of meteors, the ordinary shooting-stars, are, however, relatively faint and can be seen only at night against a moonless sky. Many additional meteors are so faint they can be seen only through binoculars or wide-angle telescopes.

Only a few thousand fireballs appear over the earth each day and, no matter how diligent the observer, he could not possibly be always alert on the chance that he might see one. Before routine photographic trapping was introduced astronomers had to rely chiefly upon the descriptions of unskilled observers who were amazed by the awe-inspiring spectacle of a great fireball bursting into view. They eloquently described what they saw, but often

---

* The American Meteor Society, organized by Professor C. P. Olivier, operates from the Flower Observatory, Upper Darby, Penn.

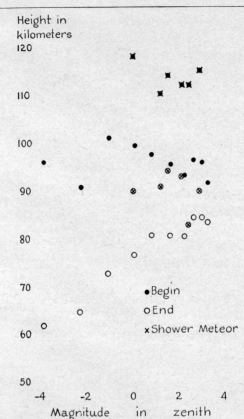

Fig. 47.—Meteor heights and magnitudes.

According to the results of the Arizona Meteor Expedition the heights at which meteors appear change little with their magnitude, but bright meteors penetrate much lower than faint ones. Shower meteors begin and end higher than sporadic meteors of equal brightness. This probably results from a difference in the composition of shower and sporadic meteors.

forgot that the astronomer needs cold facts on directions, angular elevations and durations. The astronomer's task is further complicated by the fact that our urban population often has only the haziest concepts of direction even in familiar surroundings. An interesting psychological effect frequently reported is the feeling that the meteor fell to the earth "next door," "in the next block" or "in that pile of leaves," even though it was several hundred kilometers away. By sifting and weighting numerous reports of this type astronomers can sometimes derive a bright meteor's path through the atmosphere.

Even an experienced observer is badly handicapped in studying ordinary meteors, for he never knows when or where the next one will appear. Suddenly he must locate its path among the stars and estimate its duration and brightness with high accuracy. A further complication comes through the observer's predilection to draw the trails longer or shorter than they really were or to displace them to the right or left from their true positions. Even so, the average heights at which meteors appear and disappear are well known from scientific visual observations. For the ordinary meteors the heights of appearance are consistently near ninety-five kilometers irrespective of the meteor's brightness. But the bright ones penetrate deepest into the atmosphere. Great fireballs which rival the full moon in brightness are visible to even lower levels, many to nearly forty kilometers, while those from which meteorites fall often blaze to within twenty kilometers of the ground. Meteors belonging to the strong showers, some of which meet the earth's atmosphere head-on, appear near 115 kilometers, much higher than the average meteor of the same brightness. Although part of this unusual behavior may be attributed to the high velocities of the shower members, most of it arises because they differ in composi-

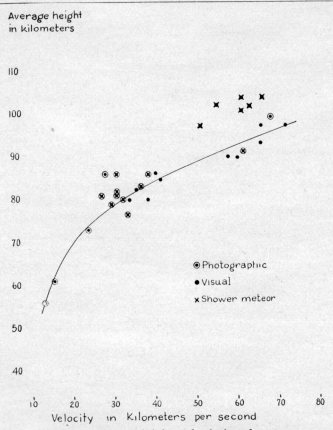

Average height
in kilometers

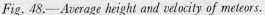

Velocity in Kilometers per second

Fig. 48.—Average height and velocity of meteors.

   The average of the beginning and ending heights of meteors is strongly
related to their velocity through the atmosphere. Solid dots represent
the results of visual observations made by the Arizona Meteor Expedition. According to these observations shower meteors are higher in the
atmosphere than sporadic meteors with the same velocity, but this difference does not occur among photographed meteors.

tion from the sporadic meteors. As we shall see this suspected difference in composition is confirmed by their
spectra.

Occasionally the reports about a fireball indicate that
it appeared as high as two hundred kilometers above the
earth. Such values are rare among the records of experienced observers and these extreme heights are now generally held under suspicion. Wylie made experiments which
required inexperienced observers to respond to artificial
fireballs and found that the observers extend the meteor's
path backward, thereby exaggerating the height at which
it appeared. Each solitary meteor has a radiant point just
as does each shower meteor, but we have more trouble
locating it. One observer will see the meteor against a
particular configuration of stars while a distant observer
sees it against another. If projected backward the two paths
cross indicating the radiant point. With that point located
and a value for the velocity we can determine the meteor's
orbit.

Velocities and Orbits

As we found for comets, the orbital speeds of meteors, V,
determine whether they are permanent members of the
solar system or have wandered in from the depths of space.
Our problem of deciding on which side of the parabolic
velocity the sporadic meteors come is complicated by the
fact that nearly all the periodic orbits in which they are
likely to move have velocities very near the parabolic
limit. For example, a particle moving with a period of
twenty-seven years, in an orbit having a semi-major axis
of nine A.U., has, at the earth's distance from the sun, a
velocity of 41.0 kilometers a second. This differs from the
critical value, 42.1 kilometers a second, by less than three
per cent. If we are to derive significant orbits, we must

have accurate velocities. Many careful scientists have tried
to find velocities from direct visual observations but
eventually concluded that they could not determine the
path lengths and durations of meteors with the required
accuracy.

Because the earth moves around the sun at 29.8 kilometers a second we run into some meteors and run away
from others. As a result the velocities of the meteors with
respect to the earth differs considerably from their speeds
with respect to the sun. In Figure 49 we let the arrow E

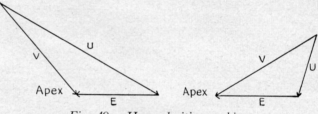

Fig. 49.—How velocities combine.

The earth's motion, E, combines with the meteor's real motion, V,
to make it enter our atmosphere with the speed and direction represented by U.

represent the earth's speed and direction around the sun.
We call the place in the sky toward which this arrow points
the apex of the earth's motion. The meteor's speed and direction we indicate by *V*. If the earth meets the meteor head-on
it rushes into the atmosphere at seventy-two kilometers a
second. If, however, the earth runs away from the meteor,
it overtakes us at only twelve kilometers a second. When
the meteor moves across the earth's orbit, *V* and *E* combine
to form the line *U* which measures the velocity and direction of the meteor's dash into the atmosphere. Not only
is the velocity of a meteor changed, but its apparent radiant
is shifted towards the earth's apex.

The earth pulls on the meteors and speeds them up to a velocity W somewhat larger than U. The amount of this effect is given by $W^2 = U^2 + 125$, when W and U are in kilometers per second. As an interesting result of this relationship we notice that even though the meteor had no original motion with respect to the earth, $U = 0$, the earth's attraction would make it strike the atmosphere at eleven kilometers a second.

Von Niessl and Hoffmeister compiled a great catalogue describing 611 fireballs. In it they list orbital velocities for more than four hundred of the meteors, and of these velocities nearly eighty per cent exceed the parabolic limit. If correct, this would mean that four out of five fireballs came from interstellar space. But we have already seen how the observations of inexperienced observers, seeing one of these great objects for the first time, are difficult to study and may give erroneous results. The highest velocities in the catalogue go with the longest paths, which in turn begin at improbably great heights, as though the real paths of the meteors had been stretched backward and the velocities magnified. The accuracy and significance of these velocities have been under discussion for years, and now there is a widespread belief that they have been exaggerated and are erroneous.

For many years attempts have been made to devise techniques by which the average heliocentric velocity of meteors could be determined from quantities accurately and easily observable. Schiaparelli pointed out in 1866 that in the morning hours we are on the forward side of the earth, Figure 50, and sweeping through the meteors at high speed. In the evening we are on the back side of the earth and we see only the meteors which overtake us at low speed. As a result the number of meteors visible per hour before dawn may be four or five times that after dusk.

The amount of this change in frequency depends upon the average heliocentric velocity of the meteors; if they move very fast the earth's motion produces little effect upon their velocity and frequency. Hoffmeister has exploited the possibilities of using this ratio as a measure of the average meteor velocity. From many observations he concludes

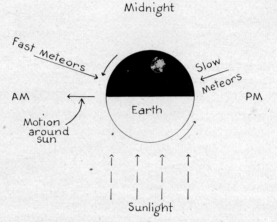

Fig. 50.—Diurnal effects upon meteors.

In the evening the observer is on the back of the moving earth and observes only meteors which overtake us. In the morning he is on the forward side and meets the meteors head-on.

that sporadic meteors move around the sun more than twice as fast as the earth does; that is, nearly all of them come from interstellar space.

Hoffmeister reaches this important conclusion on the basis of two fundamental assumptions: that the brightness of a meteor, which determines whether or not we can see it, is independent of the velocity with which the meteor enters the atmosphere; and that the meteors move through space in all directions with equal frequency. There is good evidence that neither assumption is correct. The theory of

meteor incandescence shows a great dependence of brightness upon velocity. Furthermore there is no reason to suppose that sporadic meteors do move with equal abundance
in all directions. Certainly the asteroids do not, nor do
periodic comets or meteor streams.

The importance of determining what fraction, if any, of
the sporadic meteors belong
to the solar system and in
what direction they move
stimulated a joint effort by
the Harvard Observatory
and Cornell University. In
1931 they sent an expedition
to Arizona to observe meteors and in a period of two
years under the clear skies of
that region recorded 22,000,
many of them from two
stations. In the hands of Öpik
in Estonia these records are
yielding a wealth of information on heights and mo-
tions of meteors. One
important feature of the
expedition was an attempt to
derive accurate velocities
from visual observations. A
mirror was rotated through
a small angle by a rapidly
spinning motor. The observer
looking into the mirror saw

Fig. 51.—An oscillating mirror.

One of the oscillating mirrors
used by the Arizona Meteor
Expedition in the determination
of meteor velocities. The mirror
lies on the flat table below the
telescope lens and is given an
oscillatory motion when the apex
of the supporting tripod frame is
spun around by the motor.

all the stars as little circles while a meteor flashing across the
field went through a series of loops whose size and separation
depended upon its angular velocity, Figure 52. Duplicate

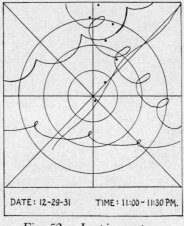

DATE: 12-29-31   TIME: 11:00 - 11:30 PM.

Fig. 52.—Looping meteors.

A typical set of wiggly trails observed through an oscillating mirror. Slow meteors go through many loops while fast meteors make only a wavy path.

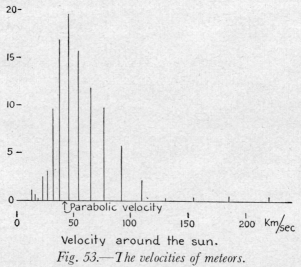

Velocity around the sun.

Fig. 53.—The velocities of meteors.

According to these results, obtained by Öpik from the observations of the Arizona Meteor Expedition, sixty-six per cent of the sporadic meteors come from interstellar space.

observations from a second station fixed the path in the atmosphere; with the known angular velocity the real velocity could then be calculated. Öpik concludes that the velocities of 1436 meteors were distributed as shown in Figure 53, where sixty-six per cent of the velocities exceed the parabolic limit marked by the arrow. From observations made through a low-power telescope and another rotating mirror Öpik thought that the fraction of hyperbolic meteors increased in the fainter magnitudes until it included nearly all meteors of the ninth magnitude. When he considered the relation between the velocities of the meteors and their directions of motion he was, however, surprised to find that, even before corrections were applied for the influence of velocity upon brightness and frequency, more hyperbolic meteors came from behind the earth than from in front. This suggests that the velocities derived may be systematically too large. The human eye is a wonderful device, but it has limitations, and the accurate placement of loops in the trails of rapidly moving meteors may be beyond our capabilities.

Meteor Photography

The possibilities of recording meteors photographically have long been recognized. The earliest meteor photograph was secured in Prague on November 27, 1885; the meteor belonged to the great Andromede shower of that year. Since then many meteors have left their marks on photographs exposed at various observatories. For more than fifty years the Harvard Observatory has systemmatically photographed the sky and accumulated nearly half a million plates which show the trails of more than a thousand bright meteors. The majority of these were recorded accidentally in the course of other routine photographic work, as in Figure 54, although a few were trapped by cameras

Fig. 54.—A typical meteor photograph.

The meteor first appears as a fine hair line, then brightens, fades and ends in a final flash.

operated especially for meteors on nights when showers were expected. If you anticipate photographing meteors, be well supplied with patience. On average nights a typical F/4.5 camera having a field of 60° traps one meteor in one hundred exposure-hours. When a strong shower develops, such as the Perseid shower in mid-August, the rate may increase to one meteor in five exposure-hours.

Fig. 55.—An interrupted meteor trail.

Each twentieth of a second a thin rotating blade occults the camera lens and breaks the meteor trail into segments. This meteor appears similar to that in Figure 54, having a central flare and a final flash

Our only precise velocities come through the use of impersonal automatic photographic records. In 1893 Elkin of Yale began a systematic program for photographing meteors from two stations. By rotating a shutter, made from a bicycle wheel, at a known rate in front of the camera lenses, he broke each meteor trail into segments which told him the meteor's velocity. Unfortunately the distance between his two stations was insufficient to yield results of satisfactory accuracy. Since then other people have photographed meteors from two stations, but no extensive attempts to determine velocities were made until recently.

At the suggestion of Whipple one of the Harvard Observatory's short-focus cameras in Cambridge and another at Oak Ridge, thirty-eight kilometers away, have operated since 1936 upon schedules so synchronized that they are both directed towards a point eighty kilometers above the earth. Any bright meteor passing near this point records itself on the two photographs. Each camera lens is occulted by a thin blade, like a windmill, which segments the photographed trails twenty times a second, thereby providing a means for accurately computing their velocities. From the duplicate photographs Whipple derives not only precise velocities but also the rate at which the meteors are slowed down as they penetrate into the denser layers of the atmosphere. This deceleration is small, in general a bit less than the amount by which the earth's attraction speeded up the meteor. Not many sporadic meteors have been photographed in duplicate, but those investigated all have velocities considerably below the parabolic limit. The orbits in Table 15 suggest that originally these meteors moved like the close-approaching asteroids.

The contrast between these velocities obtained through photography and those from visual observations is striking.

The results for bright meteors obtained from photography are precise and cannot be questioned. Fainter meteors may have high velocities, as Öpik and Hoffmeister conclude, but we cannot be certain of the answer until we can photograph them. With more efficient cameras and more sensitive photographic emulsions they will soon be recorded for study. Already third and fourth magnitude meteors are recorded by fast Schmidt-type cameras.

TABLE 15

THE AVERAGE ORBITS OF THREE PHOTOGRAPHED METEORS, THREE CLOSE-APPROACHING ASTEROIDS AND SHORT-PERIOD COMETS THAT CROSS THE EARTH'S ORBIT

	Period, years	Semi-major axis, A.U.	Peri-helion distance A.U.	Eccentric-ity	Inclina-tion
Meteors.............	3.8	2.45	0.63	0.74	4.1°
Asteroids...........	2.2	1.66	.57	.65	4.7°
Comets.............	5.4	3.06	.74	.77	20.5°

METEOR SPECTRA AND COMPOSITION

When a glass prism is placed in front of a camera, the light of a meteor can be dispersed into its component colors and photographed. Direct photography of meteors proceeds slowly, but four to five times more exposure is required to record a spectrum. Up to 1930 only eight meteor spectra had been photographed, all by accident. While at the Harvard Observatory in 1931 Millman began his routine program of spectrum photography. Within a few years several groups of amateurs joined in the work and now, principally through the efforts of observers in Canada, the Soviet Union and the United States the number of photographed spectra exceeds fifty.

Fig. 56.—A multiple meteor camera and spectrograph.

Millman uses this mounting for two fast cameras and four spectro-
graphs directed through the large rotating shutter.

In Figure 57 we see two typical meteor spectra which
consist of isolated bright lines. Only gases give such bright-
line spectra, hence the light we see arises in an envelope
of hot gas. Millman found that the spectra formed two
groups, type Y containing two strong lines, known as H
and K, due to calcium and type Z from which these lines
were absent. According to Table 16 the shower meteors
all contain calcium while the so-called sporadic meteors
are evenly divided between the two types. The chemical
elements identified in each type and the over-all frequency
with which they occur are shown in Table 17. When considering this table we must recall that some of the spectra

of low quality show only a few intense lines, usually identified with iron and calcium. Also sodium, magnesium and silicon appear well only upon panchromatic films which have just recently become sensitive enough to record meteor spectra.

The elements listed in Table 17, are, as we shall see in Chapter 9, among the most abundant in meteorites. But

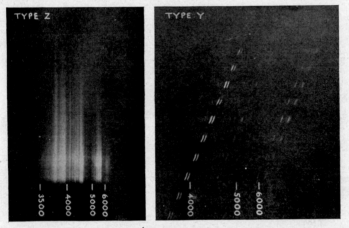

Fig. 57.—The spectra of two meteors.

On the left is type Z whose light comes principally from iron atoms. On the right is type Y with two strong radiations, near 4000, due to calcium. Other radiations are due to magnesium, silicon, sodium and iron. This spectrum was taken with the apparatus shown in Figure 56. Both spectra are on panchromatic films.

there are two varieties of meteorites: the stony ones containing oxygen, silicon, aluminum, iron, magnesium, calcium and sodium; and the metallic ones containing iron, nickel and cobalt. These match the compositions of meteors, which must be small pieces of the same stuff as meteorites.

The shower meteors, with one questionable exception, contain calcium and must be stony particles. This one

TABLE 16

THE TYPES OF FORTY-FOUR METEOR SPECTRA

Type	Y	Z
Perseid	10	
Leonid	11	1?
Geminid	3	
Orionid	1	
Sporadic	8	10
	33	11

TABLE 17

ELEMENTS FOUND IN METEOR SPECTRA

Element	Number
Iron	37
Calcium ion	33
Calcium	17
Manganese	9
Magnesium	7
Chromium	3
Magnesium ion	2
Silicon ion	2
Silicon	2
Nickel	2
Aluminium	2
Sodium	1

TABLE 18

ABUNDANCE OF MAGNESIUM, CALCIUM, SODIUM AND ALUMINUM IN FIFTY-NINE METEORITES

	Magnesium, per cent	Calcium, per cent	Sodium, per cent	Aluminium, per cent
Maximum	21.6	17.5	2.9	7.2
Minimum	4.3	0.0	0.0	0.1
Mean	14.3	1.3	0.6	1.5

exception, apparently a member of the Leonid shower, is a poor spectrum difficult to study. If we investigate the quantity of calcium present in stony meteorites, we find that it is not abundant and is sometimes completely absent, Table 18, but when calcium is absent magnesium is

Fig. 58.—Spectrum of a bright fireball.

This fireball, as bright as the quarter-moon, first appeared at a height of 125 kilometers and disappeared at 80 kilometers. On its downward path it frequently flared, the especially bright flare near the end was at a height of 94 kilometers. The spectrum is of type Z, consisting of iron and nickel.

abundant. Since magnesium is rarely recorded except on panchromatic films, this exceptional Leonid may have been a stony particle rich in magnesium which was not recorded by ordinary blue-sensitive film.

A meteor results when a little particle moving many kilometers a second smashes into the atoms and molecules of our protecting atmosphere. These atmospheric atoms

collide with the solid particle so violently that they chip
atoms from its surface and send them flying away with high
energy to form a cloud of gas with a temperature near
2000°C. This atomic pecking continues until the small solid
particle is completely consumed. Occasionally the particles
spinning around like pin-wheels make flares along their
paths, Figure 58. Others split into several parts, while some
end their existence in a final bright burst.

Average meteors never reach the ground and cannot be
weighed. But their sizes can be found from studies of how
large the particles must be to produce the light we see, for
their brightness depends chiefly upon their speed and size.
The theory indicates that the brightness of ordinary meteors
changes proportionally to the mass—a large particle makes
a bright meteor. The brightness also changes very rapidly
with velocity, the fastest moving particles making the brightest meteors. A second magnitude meteor of the Perseid
shower, velocity 61 kilometers a second, has a mass of a few
milligrams—about that of a pin-head. At the low velocity
of the Giacobinid shower, 23 kilometers a second, this same
particle would produce a meteor of only the fifth magnitude, barely visible on a clear moonless night.

METEOR TRAINS

Nearly all meteors of zero magnitude or brighter leave a
phosphorescent streak in their wake. For common meteors
the trains last little more than a second, but for very
bright meteors they last from several minutes to a half hour
or more. Immediately after the meteor passes its train
begins to expand and often within two or three seconds is a
hollow cylinder a kilometer across. When the spectrum of
such a train has eventually been photographed and studied
we shall know what the train consists of, but we already
have a few clues. Train-duration is associated not only with

the brightness of the meteor but also with its velocity; the faster, hotter meteors like the Leonids have the most conspicuous trains. Another peculiarity of the trains is their occurrence near the height of eighty-two kilometers where the temperature of the atmosphere reaches a minimum of

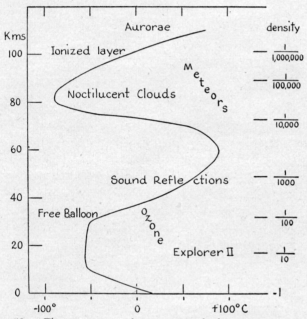

Fig. 59.—*Temperature and structure of the upper atmosphere.*

The temperatures are on the Centigrade scale which has 0° for freezing water and 100° for boiling water. The rapid drop in density is evident from the scale at the right.

— 90°C. Frequently bright meteors penetrate well below this level, but leave trains only along the small portion of their path through this region. Meteor trains are probably associated with many other phenomena occurring near this cold zone: meteors flare up most commonly at this level; radio-waves are reflected from the heavily ionized

Fig. 60.—Long-enduring sunlit train of a meteor.

This train in the wake of a bright meteor was visible for an hour and a half as it hung high above the earth in sunlight after twilight had fallen on the ground below. The train was 600 kilometers from the photographer in Chicoutimi, Canada.

Kennelly-Heaviside layer near this height; noctilucent clouds, rarely seen in America, occur there; and auroral streamers and arcs extend upward from this region. All of these phenomena, some of which are electrical, are probably related to each other and to the formation and preservation of self-luminous meteor trains.

Radio-engineers are now inquiring about the frequency and energy of bright meteors, for they may cause certain types of static. Jansky and Skellet of the Bell Telephone Laboratory thought their short-wave receivers gave a hiss each time a bright meteor appeared. Recently J. A. Pierce, who studies the earth's radio-roof by bouncing very short-waves on it, found spurious, short-lived reflections from low altitudes. These too come when bright meteors dash through the atmosphere smashing molecules and atoms apart creating a miniature ionosphere. The time may come when the astronomer, in dressing gown and slippers, will sit by his radio on cloudy nights or during the daytime listening to meteors.

There is another type of meteor train—great sunlit trains that are clouds of smoke and dust. These occur only in the wake of very bright meteors, those likely to drop meteorites, which penetrate to the lower regions of the atmosphere. Since such bright fireballs are rare and only a few of them leave great quantities of dust and debris along their paths, smoke trains are among the rarest of meteoric phenomena. The most conspicuous sunlit trains occur at twilight when they, being high in the atmosphere, are illuminated by the sun, while the observers below are in darkness. One such train over eastern Canada is shown in Figure 60; the original photograph was taken by a quick-minded amateur using an inexpensive camera. The train was visible for an hour and a half, but this seems to be the only photograph made of it. When compared with visual observations from distant places this picture showed that the train was 600 kilometers from the observer, at a height from forty-eight to eighty kilometers over the southern tip of Hudson's Bay.

One interesting feature of all meteor trains is their rapid deformation, turning from straight lines into twisted forms within a few minutes after their appearance. Such writhings demonstrate the existence of winds in the high upper atmosphere, winds with hurricane velocities of two hundred kilometers an hour.

COUNTING METEORS

On a clear moonless night a single observer will see about ten meteors per hour; the actual number depends upon the time of night, the season of the year and the blackness of the sky. Although this rate may seem small to the observer, it indicates a tremendous number of similar meteors appearing over the whole earth per day. The observer's field of view is about sixty degrees in diameter which, at an altitude of eighty kilometers, covers an area of five thousand square kilometers. Since the total area of the atmosphere is approximately five hundred million square kilometers, we see one meteor in each hundred thousand; our ten meteors per hour means a total of twenty-four million over the whole earth each day.

Twenty-four million meteors visible each day is a sizable catch for a tiny body like the earth. Yet the real total far exceeds this, for many faint meteors are not noticed by the observers while other fainter ones can be seen only through telescopes. If the observer carefully records how many meteors of each magnitude he sees, he will find the greatest numbers at the third and fourth magnitudes. According to his records the total number of each magnitude each day over the earth would be very near those in column two of Table 19. But this typical observer and every other observer fails to notice many faint meteors at the edge of his field of view. Öpik compared the records of four near-by but independent observers and found each recorded nine-tenths of the meteors of the third magnitude, one half those of the fourth magnitude and one twelfth those of the fifth magnitude. When the observed numbers are corrected for these omissions, the total daily numbers become those in the third column. We find there that the meteors of the fifth magnitude and brighter total seventy-five million per day.

Through binoculars or a low-power telescope we can observe many additional faint meteors. For example through a four-inch telescope having a field nearly four degrees across we see about five meteors an hour. At a height of eighty kilometers our telescope takes in an area of twenty-five square kilometers; thus the number of meteors of the tenth magnitude and brighter must be a

TABLE 19

THE NUMBER AND MASS OF METEORS STRIKING THE EARTH EACH DAY

Visual magnitude	*Observed number*	*True number*	*Mass, milligrams*	*Total mass, kilograms*
−3	28,000	28,000	4,000	11
−2	71,000	71,000	1,600	11
−1	180,000	180,000	630	11
0	450,000	450,000	250	11
1	1,100,000	1,100,000	100	11
2	2,800,000	2,800,000	40	11
3	6,400,000	7,100,000	16	11
4	9,000,000	18,000,000	6.3	11
5	3,600,000	45,000,000	2.5	11
6		110,000,000	1.0	11
7		280,000,000	0.40	11
8		710,000,000	0.16	11
9		1,800,000,000	0.063	11
10		4,500,000,000	0.025	11

hundred times that of the fifth magnitude—or a total of several billion. By carefully noting their magnitudes we find that the number increases 2.5 times with each fainter magnitude, or one hundred times for five magnitude steps. With this rate of increase we may extend Table 19 to the tenth magnitude and find a total of eight billion meteors entering the earth's atmosphere daily.

The total fall of meteoric material, from the fireballs dropping meteorites to the faintest telescopic meteors, can be found when we know the masses of the individual meteors at each magnitude. Knowing the mass of a second magnitude meteor and assuming the average velocity as fifty-five kilometers a second, we find the average mass of a typical meteor of zero magnitude to be 250 milligrams— the weight of a few drops of water. Since the brightness of a meteor changes with its mass, a fifth magnitude meteor, giving only one per cent as much light as one of zero magnitude, arises from a particle of 2.5 milligrams. When we put these values into Table 19 the total mass for each magnitude interval comes out constant.

To obtain the total mass we need not add up the contributions of a very great number of magnitudes. The very largest bodies crash through the atmosphere and fall to the earth as meteorites. In Chapter 8 we shall add up their mass and find it to be about 550 kilograms a day, which represents all the meteors brighter than magnitude −10. At the other extreme we find a limiting magnitude beyond which there can be few, if any, meteors. Tiny dust particles are blown away from the solar system by the sun's radiation pressure which we have seen produces comets' tails. The smallest particle that can strike the earth at the lowest possible speed, eleven kilometers a second, produces a meteor of the thirtieth magnitude. There can be no meteors fainter. From Table 19 we sum the mass of meteors over the magnitude interval −10 to +30 and add the meteorites; the resulting total daily mass of meteoric material is only 1000 kilograms—one ton. Each day the earth sweeps up a truck load of sand and gravel which is uniformly spread over its surface. In the two billion years since the earth was formed the accumulation of meteors at this rate would total only one thousand tons per square kilometer, which would make a layer less than a centimeter thick over the whole earth.

7

METEOR SHOWERS

A MAGNIFICENT DISPLAY OF SHOOTING STARS STARTLED THE inhabitants of the Americas on November 12, 1833. Beginning before midnight the meteors increased in frequency until at dawn they were as thick as snow flakes. A single observer often saw twenty appear within a second. Many superstitious people thought this marked the end of the world, and as bells tolled they prepared for the future. Next day all was serene, but a new branch of astronomy, the study of meteors, had been founded.

This great display and the others that occur from time to time present some of the most interesting but tantalizing information we have about the occupants of interplanetary space. We know nothing of these flying gravel banks until we collide with them and have a great meteor shower. Even afterward we cannot accurately trace their paths through space to predict when we may encounter them again for when between the planets they are invisible to us. The earth is playing a game of cosmic blind-man's buff with them; only if by chance we tunnel into one of these swarms of particles does a brilliant meteor shower result, otherwise we go swinging around the sun, completely ignorant of where or how the meteor swarms are moving.

Fig. 61.—The Leonid shower of 1833.

The appearance of the Leonid meteors on November 13, 1833 according-
ing to a contemporary artist.

After 1833 the Leonids were less numerous each year until soon the shower was quite inconspicuous. According to diaries unusual numbers of meteors had appeared in November for a few years preceding 1833; it appears that the earth cuts through the great swarm of bodies several years in a row, then misses them for many years. On November 11, 1799 Humboldt had observed a similar shower over

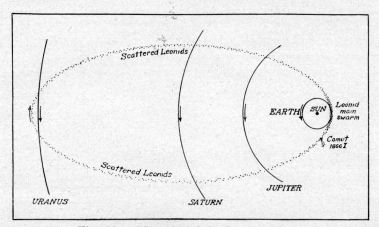

Fig. 62.—The orbit of the Leonid meteors.

This great swarm requires thirty-three years to move around its path. The meteors are so far extended along the orbit that the earth cuts through the dense part of the swarm several years in a row.

South America. This suggested that the display reappeared in November at intervals of thirty-three or thirty-four years. With these clues H. A. Newton traced the shower back through history as far as 902 A.D. when it occurred on October 20th; planetary perturbations gradually altered the orbit and changed the date of the shower. At intervals of thirty-three years between 902 and 1833 some record of unusual numbers of meteors in mid-November has been found.

According to this periodicity another shower should have come in 1866. Several years earlier it began to build up and appeared on schedule with an intensity equal to the shower of 1833. Consequently thirty-three years later astronomers and laymen alike were anticipating the greatest display of celestial fireworks of their lives. Alas! they were disappointed. Between 1866 and 1899 the meteors passed near both Saturn and Jupiter; these planets pulled the particles aside so that the earth passed through only the fringes of the swarm. As 1932 approached and the possibility of another shower was apparent many people hoped that some perturbation had swung the particles into their previous orbit. As in 1899 the meteors came at the rate of one a minute, but compared to the earlier displays this was disappointing. It is not likely that we shall again witness great displays from this stream. The earth is a mere speck in space which the meteors can easily pass without striking. The chances that as the perturbations change the meteors' orbit they will again collide with the earth are about equal to the chance that a searchlight capriciously playing over a crowd will again shine on a particular person.

The radiant point of the Leonid meteor shower is within six degrees of the direction towards which the earth is moving in its path around the sun. Since, in November, this region of the sky does not rise until near midnight the meteors from that direction do not appear until the morning hours. The Leonids meet the earth head-on entering the atmosphere at the high speed of 72 km/sec. An unusually large number of them leave streaks or enduring trains in their paths.

In the century since 1833 many other meteor showers have been recognized. Some appear regularly each year, others like the Leonids at longer intervals, while some have appeared only once or twice. Almost immediately after the Leonid shower of 1833 the unusual number of meteors in early August was recognized as due to a shower radiating from the constellation Perseus. Each year with perfect regularity meteors stream from Perseus for several weeks, reaching a maximum frequency on August 12. During more than a century the annual number of Perseids has changed so little that we are hard-put to detect their period of motion around the sun. Instead of a condensed cluster like the Leonids, the Perseids constitute a great stream of meteors uniformly spaced along their orbit. From the position of their radiant point we can derive an approximate orbit which has one especially interesting feature; the orbit is tilted almost at right angles to the plane of the earth's motion. Only by accident do they pass through the orbit of the earth, which is too small to perturb them appreciably. At no time do they pass near a large planet. We may conclude, therefore, that the Perseids have been moving in much the same path for a great interval of time during which they have gradually become uniformly spread around their entire orbit.

COMETARY ASSOCIATION

In 1862 a comet faintly visible without a telescope moved across the northern sky. As a comet it was nothing unusual, but in 1866 Schiaparelli noticed that its orbit was almost identical with that of the Perseids. This discovery strongly hinted that the meteor showers and comets were genetically related. When the orbit of the faint comet of 1866 was published Peters, Schiaparelli and von Oppolzer simultaneously saw that it had the same path as the Leonids. This second identification set off a real hunt for other pairs of comets and meteor showers moving in identical orbits. Soon the Lyrid meteors, another reliable shower appearing late in April, were identified with Comet 1861 I. Other

TABLE 20
The Orbits of Meteor Showers and Associated Comets

	Ω	ω	i	e	q, A.U.	P, years	U km/sec.
Perseids........	138°	155°	116°	0.96	0.964	108	61
Comet 1862 III.	138°	153°	114°	0.960	0.963	122	
Photographed Meteor......	142°	156°	120°	0.96	0.97	109.5	61.3, Whipple
Leonids........	233°	179°	163°	.905	.986	33.25	72
Comet 1866 I...	231°	171°	163°	.905	.977	33.18	
Lyrids........	30°	213°	80°	1.0†	0.90	......	51
Comet 1861 I...	30°	213°	80°	.984	.921	415	
Bielids........	246°	222°	13.1°	0.75	0.858	......	16
Biela's Comet, 1852 III.....	246°	223°	12.6°	0.756	.861	6.62	
Photographed Meteor......	242°	227°	12.1°	0.792*	.855*	8.3*	16.8*, Elkin
Geminids......	259°	326°	34°	1.0†	0.092	......	49
Photographed Meteor......	262°	324°	23.3°	.91	.14	1.8	35.1, Whipple
Eta Aquarids...	45°	100°	162°	.967	.595	......	66
Halley's Comet..	57°	112°	162°	.967	.587	76	
Orionids.......	28°	143°	161°	1.0†	.516	......	68
Halley's Comet.	57°	112°	162°	.967	.587	76	
Giacobinids.....	196°	175°	31°	0.710	1.016	6.6	20
Comet Giacobini-Zinner, 1933 III	196°	172°	31°	.716	1.000	6.60	
Taurids (ptg)...	47°	109°	4.5°	0.824	0.394	3.33	27.3, Whipple
Encke's Comet..	335°	185°	12.6°	.850	.332	3.28	
Delta Aquarids..	305°	.....	56°	1.0†	0.039	......	50
Quadrantids....	282°	.....	85°	1.0†	0.99	......	46

* *Somewhat uncertain.*
† *Assumed parabolic.*

periodic comets that pass near the earth's orbit were placed on the list of suspects and each newly-recognized shower was compared with them for possible identification. The number of coincident orbits has increased until now nine listed in Table 20 are unquestionably associated. We have thus good reason to conclude that each meteor stream originates from a comet.

One identification, between the Taurid meteors and Encke's Comet, has come within the past year. Whipple made the discovery from the velocities and orbits he derived for several Taurids caught in the Harvard photographic meteor traps. From visual observations Hoffmeister and others concluded that these meteors radiating from Taurus in November originated in interstellar space. Their most convincing evidence was the small rate at which the radiant changed its position from day to day as though the meteors, moving very rapidly, were little influenced by the speed or direction at which the earth encountered them. This effect could, however, also result if they were moving in a short-period orbit turned in just the right way. In 1937 and 1938 fourteen Taurids were photographed, five of them in duplicate from Cambridge and Oak Ridge. Whipple computed their orbits and found that they travelled around the sun in only 3.3 years. His further computations revealed that in the long past, some ten thousand years ago, they were associated with Encke's Comet. This interesting result must mean that Encke's Comet, which we mentioned in Chapter 4, has been moving in essentially its present orbit for many thousands of years. Around its path moves a great diffuse swarm of particles whose orbits through perturbations are gradually becoming less like the comet's.

Halley's Comet, in addition to being one of the most conspicuous comets, also provides us with not one, but two meteor showers. In May meteors radiate from Aquarius near the star Eta and in October another shower comes from the head of Orion. Both showers, according to Olivier, move in nearly the same orbit as Halley's Comet—we run into the meteors as they are approaching and leaving perihelion. Such a double shower can result only if the original orbit is turned in a particular manner such that the meteors are at the earth's distance from the sun each

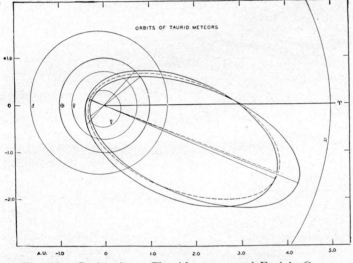

Fig. 63.—Paths of two Taurid meteors and Encke's Comet.

Through photography these meteors have been found to move around the sun with periods of only 3.3 years.

time they cross the earth's plane of motion; Halley's Comet is turned in this way. Since in October (when the Orionid meteors appear), the earth is fifteen million kilometers from the comet's orbit, the meteors must be very widely scattered. The Eta Aquarids and the Orionids are almost equally abundant each year when they appear during a period of more than a week. This is what we would expect if the earth did cut through the outer fringes of a very widely scattered stream. Halley's Comet undergoes rather periodic perturbations which would aid in scattering along its orbit any particles that strayed a bit ahead or behind.

THE BIELIDS

Short-period comets as well as those like Halley's and 1866 I also provide meteor showers. As early as 1832 astronomers noted that the orbit of Biela's comet passed within a few thousand kilometers of the earth's path, see Figure 29, and that a collision might occur, but it never did. When the orbit of a comet is known, we can compute the date and radiant point at which associated meteors should appear. As early as 1798 Brandes observed on the proper date a strong shower which probably was due to this comet. During the next decades a few other meteors moving in the comet's orbit appeared from Andromeda but nothing spectacular happened until 1872, twenty years after the comet disappeared. During all this time the earth and the comet had been playing tag; sometimes we nearly collided, but never quite succeeded. Between 1852 and 1885 the comet did not pass near Jupiter and its remains should have continued in the orbit they had in 1852. Any year we might have run into a dense swarm of meteors, but which year could not be foretold.

When darkness fell over Europe on November 27, 1872 faint meteors were pouring from the vicinity of Gamma Andromeda. For a few hours this cosmic blizzard increased in intensity as Figure 64 shows, until at 8:30 P.M. a single observer could see a hundred meteors a minute. After this peak the number decreased rapidly and by midnight, Greenwich time, only a few stragglers appeared. Observers in the western hemisphere saw only the end of the shower, but that was strong enough to thrill them. When this shower burst over the earth the comet was many thousand kilometers away, for it had passed the junction of the orbits on September 9, eighty days before the earth. These meteors move in a short-period orbit of low inclination which brings them up behind the earth, so that they enter the atmosphere at a velocity of only twenty kilometers a second. That a majority of the meteors of the shower were

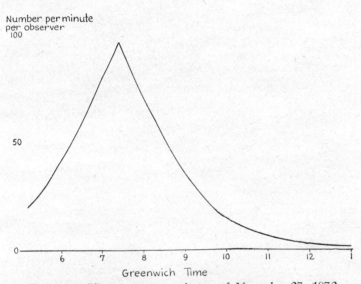

Fig. 64.—The great meteor shower of November 27, 1872.

These meteors, originally part of Biela's Comet, provided intense showers in 1872 and 1885. Since then they have shunned the earth.

faint, is undoubtedly related to this fact, their average magnitude was about the third while the Leonids and Perseids, coming head-on with higher velocity, average about the zero or first magnitude.

In 1878 the earth arrived a half-year before and in 1879 a half-year after the comet crossed the earth's orbit in mid-May, 1879. Very few meteors were seen either year. After one more complete period the comet was due to pass its node again in mid-January 1886. On November 27, 1885 another celestial blizzard appeared and again European observers had the best show. The meteor frequency was almost identical with that in 1872 and the duration of the shower was also similar. Again the majority of the meteors were faint, although an occasional one was very bright. During this shower the first photograph of a meteor was secured by Weinek at Prague. We cannot tell precisely when these meteors moved out of the comet, but H. A. Newton thought the swarms we encountered in 1872 and 1885 started their independent careers in 1841 when the comet passed near Jupiter and its ultimate disintegration began. This may be correct, but the shower of 1798 must have broken away earlier, possibly in 1772 when the comet had also passed near Jupiter. Certainly the comet was at least a century in disintegrating so completely that it could no longer be seen. In 1890 and again in 1901 Jupiter exerted its influence upon the motions of the particles. A few members of this shower appeared in 1892 and in 1899 but since then we have had no trace of them. They continue to swing around the sun passing the earth at a few million kilometers as a great undetectable flying gravel bank.

THE GIACOBINIDS

A modern counterpart of the Bielids appeared on October 9, 1933. Again as dusk fell over Europe the sky was filled with faint meteors. Their numbers increased for only a short time until at 8 P.M. Greenwich time 350 appeared each minute. Within an hour their frequency dropped to a tenth this maximum and before midnight, European time, when darkness came in America, the shower was over. The radiant point of these meteors was in the head of Draco, just where it should be if they were moving in the orbit of the short-period comet Giacobini-

Zinner discovered in 1900. Numerous people photographed members of the shower, but an all-time high was recorded at Bergedorf where one exposure of ten minutes covering a field ten degrees on a side showed twenty-six trails.

This new shower-comet pair did not come as a complete surprise, for in 1926 Denning saw enough meteors to reveal

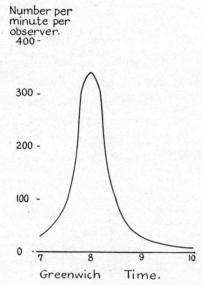

Greenwich   Time.

Fig. 65.—The meteor shower of October 9, 1933.

The meteors of this brief, but very intense shower came from the short-period comet Giacobini-Zinner.

the radiant. Jupiter continued shifting the comet's orbit and decreased the clearance between it and earth's path, Table 21. In 1933 the earth passed through the junction of the orbits eighty days after the comet, which was then 230 million kilometers away. Unlike Biela's Comet, Giacobini's has not disappeared and we can observe what orbital changes it undergoes as well as how it changes in appearance. Perhaps it will disappear, but the complete disruption

TABLE 21
CHANGES IN THE PERIHELION DISTANCE OF COMET GIACOBINI-ZINNER
A.U.

1900	0.9319
1913	.9759
1926	.9937
1933	.9997
1940	.9964

of a comet is not imminent even though meteors are scattered widely along its orbit—please notice that Halley's Comet is one of the brightest we know yet each year we meet thousands of meteors moving along its orbit.

In 1940 Comet Giacobini-Zinner crossed the earth's orbit on February 23. In 1939 the earth reached the intersection nearly a half-year early and in 1940 a half-year late, at neither time were any meteors seen from the shower radiant. Apparently the meteors are still closely grouped around this comet. In 1946, unless there are large perturbations in the interval, the earth will pass through the orbital intersection only eight days after the comet. What will result we do not know and hesitate to guess. In 1899 everyone was anticipating a magnificent shower of Leonids, but Jupiter had altered their orbit enough to prevent a direct hit on the center of the swarm. The disappointment that followed this fiasco nearly put an end to the study of meteors; only recently has much interest in them redeveloped. Consequently we are wary of predicting what will happen on October 9, 1946, but we hope that despite the nearly full moon which will illuminate the heavens the meteors will pour from the sky.

METEOR SHOWERS AND COMETS

The numerous agreements in Table 20 may suggest that each and every shower is known to be associated with a comet and similarly that every comet can provide a shower. Both suspicions are incorrect. For example, on August 31, 1935 a brief but fairly intense shower radiated from Auriga, but no known periodic comet has a similar orbit. Very likely the tiny swarm once belonged to a comet which disappeared a few centuries ago leaving its remnants to continue moving around the sun like a moth in the night.

The Geminid meteors of December are numerous each year, yet we cannot attribute them to any comet. Their short-period, 1.76 years, and small perihelion distance, 0.14 A.U., derived by Whipple from a Geminid photographed in duplicate, differ considerably from any comet known. Similarly the Quadrantids, named for an old constellation now included within Bootes, and the Delta Aquarids are other streams as yet unidentified; both have highly inclined orbits and probably have periods of about a century. Who knows but what the next new comet found may be the parent of one of these streams?

To show the great extent chance has played in these identifications we need only recount the circumstances by which the first three became possible. Precisely when the orbits of meteor showers were being determined three faint comets appeared. The first of these, 1861 I—Lyrids— has a long period orbit and will not be visible again for a century or more. Comet 1862 III—Perseids—also has a period exceeding a hundred years and will not return until the end of this century. Comet 1866 I—Leonids—has a period of thirty-three years, but in both 1899 and 1932 it was so situated in the sky that it could not be observed. Thus just at the most opportune moment these three comets appeared. If they had passed undiscovered then, we should be wondering if the meteors widely spread over these long-period orbits had ever been associated with a comet and whether the comets were still existing or defunct. What odd conclusions we might have drawn regarding the origin and past history of these streams!

Table 20 sums our knowledge of associated comets and meteor swarms accumulated during more than a century. We find there the Bielid meteors, yet none have been observed since the start of this century. A similar list prepared in 1925 would not have included the Giacobinids, yet at the present moment they are one of the strongest and most interesting showers known. A few faint meteors from Comet Pons-Winnecke were observed in 1916, 1921 and 1927, but there is little chance that we shall have a strong shower from this comet and it has not been included in this list.

When we consider the great number of comets that cross the earth's orbit the number that supply meteor showers is small. None of the near-parabolic orbits have been identified with any shower; probably because they are not enough disturbed by planetary perturbations to loosen up; even if they are, the particles are thinly spread around the vast orbit and are not recognized as a meteor shower. According to Figure 28 the majority of periodic comets stay outside the earth's orbit and cannot supply meteor streams. Those that do cross the earth's orbit are, however, generous with their meteors. All these comets have short-period orbits which undergo many perturbations and rapid disintegration. Their low inclinations keep them near the earth's plane and as the particles spread out our chances of encountering at least some of the out-riders of the swarms is good.

Those showers selected for mention in Tables 14 and 20 are only the richer more prominent ones. For each of them dozens of weaker showers appear, but their reality is difficult to establish because the few meteors they provide are almost lost among the frequent sporadic meteors. The definitions and rules by which a real shower radiant can be identified have been the subject of much debate, but it is evident that the difficulties lie in distinguishing the shower radiant, found by projecting the trails backward until they cross, from an accidental grouping of the places at which unrelated sporadic meteor trails cross. When an observer sees and imperfectly records three or four meteors of a weak shower among perhaps a hundred sporadic meteors, he has great difficulty in making certain that the shower was real. As another complication, many showers catch up with the earth from behind, as do the short-period comets, therefore they have low velocities and their meteors are faint and infrequent. To circumvent some of these difficulties Öpik devised a statistical method by which he could evaluate the chance that any given set of meteors really composed a shower. From 2000 apparent radiants he selected 279 that were probably real. Of the 31 strongest showers included 29 have orbits which bring them against the forward side of the earth. If however, we derive parabolic orbits from the 279 radiants, we find that 65 per cent of the showers came from behind the earth. The effects of velocity emphasize the streams meeting the earth head-on by making their meteors more numerous and brighter, but the great majority of the streams move in direct orbits of low inclinations, as do the short-period comets with which they are probably associated.

The distances between the particles forming a meteor swarm are amazingly large and remind us of the small amount of material with which we are dealing. At the Perseid shower maximum a single observer watching some five thousand square kilometers of atmosphere will see about one meteor per minute. Each of these meteors, weighing a few milligrams, is the sole occupant of a space containing over ten million cubic kilometers. On the average the particles are separated by over two hundred kilometers. Similarly H. A. Newton estimated that in the great Leonid shower of 1866 the particles were thirty kilometers apart; while within the densest part of the Bielid clusters the particles averaged forty kilometers apart. In contrast to these relatively dense clusters and streams the average separation of sporadic meteors is about five hundred kilometers.

The total amount of material comprising all the meteors scattered around the Perseid orbit can now be estimated. Let us assume that for one full day the Perseids appear at their maximum rate and that each particle weighs 25 milligrams. The total amount of material scattered along the orbit comes out around five hundred million tons, which would make a layer two centimeters thick over the state of Connecticut. This is then a minimum value for the mass of the comet before the meteors began to scatter around its path.

Formation of Meteor Streams

One point about the evolution of a meteor stream seems to be clear. At first the meteors are close to or part of the parent comet. As planetary perturbations gradually influence them they stray away, moving in practically the same orbit as the comet but running ahead or behind. Given sufficient time they become uniformly distributed around the orbit. The Perseids seem to represent the full development of this process which, due to their high orbital inclination, has proceeded without too many serious planetary influences. The Taurids represent perhaps the farthest extreme we can recognize for the short-period comets. They are fairly evenly distributed around their orbit, but they have undergone so many planetary perturbations that their orbits differ appreciably from that of the parent comet.

Fig. 66.—A bright Geminid meteor.

This meteor was so bright it cast shadows. It progressed from left to right, passed north of the Pleiades near the center of the picture and split as it neared the end of its path.

Furthermore they have been dispersed through such a large volume that we seldom encounter enough to make a recognizable shower. The Andromedes from Biela's Comet are going through the same process, but still travel as small clusters only a few hundred thousand kilometers across. The chances that the earth will encounter a swarm of this size are very small and many such swarms must move between the planets and remain unknown to us until by accident we collide.

In the previous chapter we considered how the velocity
of a meteor influenced its brightness and observability.
Within a shower all the velocities are equal and the distribution of magnitudes measures the number of particles
of different sizes. Over a range of eight magnitudes the
frequency of Giacobinid meteors seemed to increase uniformly 2.5 times with each magnitude. The eight magnitudes are equivalent to a range of a thousand in the masses
of the particles, or a factor of ten in their diameters. In
the Leonid and Perseid showers faint meteors, especially
those visible only through binoculars or a telescope, are
rare; the same is true for the Geminids. These streams seem
to contain few small particles. Large particles also are rare
among the showers meteors, which seldom present us with
a tremendous fireball. Furthermore no meteorite has been
identified as coming from any known shower.

We have then what seems good evidence that the particles
have been sorted according to their sizes and only those of
comparable size move together. We cannot attribute this
effect to the radiation pressure of sunlight, for it is inef-
fective with particles of this size. Collisions between large
and small bodies in a swarm or with stray bodies moving
through space will effect the motions of the small bodies
more than the large ones, but such collisions will be rare
when the tiny particles are separated by hundreds of
kilometers. A more effective means of winnowing out the
small particles comes through the Poynting-Robertson
effect found in the theory of relativity. All of the particles
are illuminated by sunlight. As they become warm, they
re-radiate heat into space in all directions. But the radiation
in the direction of the particles's motion pushes back on it
thereby retarding its motion. The amount of this effect
depends greatly upon the particle's size, small particles are
retarded most rapidly. Since a change in velocity results

in a change in orbit, within a few thousand years the smaller members of a stream move quite differently from the larger bodies. We have then a stratification or segregation according to size which combines with the other effects operating to dissipate meteor swarms.

There is no doubt that the meteor showers, whether recurring annually or at intervals of many years, are associated with comets. From their spectra we know that the shower meteors are small stony particles. Presumably they are typical constituents of comets, but the nucleus of a comet may contain larger masses that we are not likely to encounter. How the vast number of small stony chips were organized as a comet and sent flying in a large orbit is one of many difficult problems to be explained when we account for the existence of the solar system.

8

A METEORITE FALLS

A GREAT FIREBALL ABRUPTLY FLARING INTO VIEW MAY not be completely consumed in its mad dash through the atmosphere, but a remnant sometimes falls to the earth below. These chunks of stone and metal, the meteorites, are the only solid material from outer space to reach the earth and our laboratories. Through careful study of how they reached the earth and of their composition and structure we may be able to learn what types of material move between the planets and what their past history has been.

Only a few new meteorites are recognized each year but the total known is now fourteen hundred. Each is identified by the name of the nearest town or prominent landmark, thus establishing the place of discovery as well as the identity. Since meteorites are found in all parts of the world their names constitute a veritable geography lesson, including Joe Wright Mountain (Arkansas), Willy Willy (Australia), Bustee (India) and Prambachkirchen (Austria).

New meteorites are recognized through two processes; some are seen to fall and immediately recovered, and others are accidentally found and subsequently recognized as meteorites. In statistical discussions these two modes of discovery must be carefully distinguished. Further complications arise from the variations in composition. Yet the fourteen hundred known meteorites form only three distinct groups, those composed of metal, those of stone and more rarely those of the two materials in roughly equal proportion. The dense metallic masses, composed principally of nickel-iron, immediately reveal themselves as unusual material wherever found. In contrast the stony

Fig. 67.—A meteorite falls.

From painting by Benson B. Moore, courtesy of The Sky.

masses, differing but little from ordinary rocks in density and appearance, pass unnoticed upon casual inspection. From Table 22 we see that among found meteorites the great majority are metallic, or irons, while among the witnessed falls stones predominate by ten to one. In regions where a dense population has existed for a long time, the fraction of irons among the total meteorites is low, for those that fell centuries ago have been collected and destroyed by use as implements. The proportion of irons in India is only three per cent, in Japan twelve per cent and in Europe fourteen per cent. Over recently settled areas the fraction

TABLE 22
FREQUENCY OF METEORITE FINDS AND FALLS

Type	Finds		Falls	
	Number	Per cent	Number	Per cent
Irons..........................	409	66	29	5
Stony-irons...................	46	7½	8	1½
Stones.......................	165	26½	547	93½
Total.....................	620		584	

of irons runs much higher, for North America it is sixty-nine per cent and for Australia eighty-one per cent. Arid regions devoid of trees and undergrowth favor the preservation and later discovery of metallic meteorites, for rusting and disintegration proceed there at a minimum rate. Of 111 meteorites from India 108 were seen to fall while of 43 from Chile not one was witnessed!

How Meteorites Hit the Earth

Our astronomical information about fireballs dropping meteorites is very poor, which is hardly surprising as we must depend upon the observations of untrained people startled by the unheralded apparition. Velocities have been derived for a few fireballs producing meteorites, but the results obtained, like those for fireballs in general, are of questionable accuracy. Apparently the most reliable velocity was derived for the Pultusk stones which fell in Poland January 30, 1868. From many observations, some by professional astronomers, Galle derived an atmospheric velocity of 27.5 kilometers per second, for which the velocity around the sun of fifty-seven kilometers a second corresponds to a decidedly hyperbolic orbit. Yet the

Fig. 68.—The Plainview meteorite from Texas.

These two stones found a half mile apart fit together perfectly. (*Photo by H. H. Nininger.*)

beginning height of 280 kilometers is very large and recalls the stretching effect distorting the velocities of the fireballs listed in the von Niessl-Hoffmeister Katalog. Whether the meteorites originated in interstellar space or are permanent members of the solar system is a fundamental cosmological question that can be settled only by indisputable velocities and orbits yet to be obtained.

Even so, from the radiant points of fireballs that dropped meteorites some information about their orbits can be found. From 116 cases H. A. Newton concluded that the great majority of meteorites overtook the earth in direct orbits of low inclination and large perihelion distance. In such orbits the meteorites enter the atmosphere with very low velocities which minimize their chances of being disrupted. A few meteorites do survive head-on collision with the earth, but usually at the cost of being shattered into thousands of fragments. In several cases, such as the Plainview meteorite, Figure 68, some of the fragments can be fitted together to form a single mass.

According to Figure 69 meteorite falls are observed most frequently in the afternoon and during the summer months. The predominance of afternoon over morning falls is

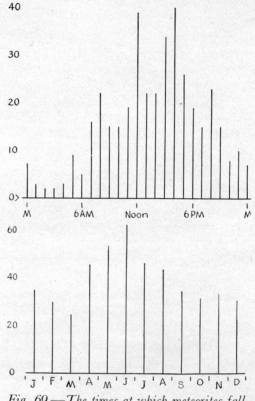

Fig. 69.—The times at which meteorites fall.

Above: The times of observed meteorite falls according to the hour of the day; the maximum rate is in mid-afternoon. Below: The times of observed meteorite falls according to month; the maximum rate is closely associated with the duration of daylight in the northern hemisphere.

probably significant, for in the afternoon the point in space from which the earth is moving as it goes around the sun is above the horizon. W. J. Fisher has shown that the predominance of day-time over night-time and of summer over winter falls results from the presence of sunshine, whereby the falling material is seen or the dust it raises at impact attracts attention. At night when fireballs are most conspicuous, meteorites are rarely recovered unless they happen to strike buildings; a few such cases are known. In 1847 one of the Braunau irons weighing twenty-one kilograms fell through a bedroom without harming the three children sleeping there. Incidentally, there are no authentic cases on record in which people have been killed by falling meteorites; there are, however, some records of domestic animals having been struck.

It is difficult to associate a meteorite falling during the afternoon with the strong meteor showers which appear late at night and we know of no meteorite which has fallen from such a shower. Many meteorites may come from showers which over-take the earth and are too weak to be recognized, but only after we have accurate velocities and orbits for meteorites can we discover what relation they have to comets and meteor swarms.

During the past decade the number of meteorite discoveries has increased rapidly, at present the rate averages twenty-five a year. Such a rate has, however, not been true in the past. Occasionally one or more years have passed without the discovery of a single new meteorite; in the four consecutive years 1906, 1907, 1908 and 1909 only one new meteorite was reported. A precise count of the meteorites known at any time is difficult to obtain for new bodies may be discovered but not recognized or reported for several years. Again what appear to be two different but adjacent meteorites may, after careful study, prove to be from the same parent mass. The present high rate of discovery indicates an increased interest in meteorites; people are becoming meteorite conscious.

In the United States the majority of discoveries result from the work of the Society for Research on Meteorites, especially the work of its president, H. H. Nininger, who,

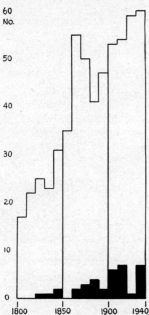

from his Denver base, tours the mid-western plain states lecturing about and exhibiting meteorites. Through these efforts many old as well as freshly fallen specimens have been recognized. Although Nininger has a number of persons assisting him, he does not rely solely upon their efforts. As soon as a great detonating fireball likely to have dropped meteorites is reported he travels to the region and interviews the observers. From their reports he defines the probable fall-area and either surveys it personally or enlists the active aid of the community.

Fig. 70.—The frequency of observed meteorite falls by decades.

In this manner numerous freshly fallen meteorites are recovered in spite of the fact that they fell at night or far from any observer. At present Nininger is accounting for half of all the discoveries in the world. The fruitfulness of the plain regions can best be appreciated by comparing its stone-free widely-cultivated soil with the rocky, wooded

From 1800 to the present the number of observed meteorite falls has constantly increased as people became "meteorite conscious". The black areas represent metallic meteorites and the white areas stony meteorites.

hillsides of New England where only five meteorites, all witnessed falls, have been collected.

Fig. 71.—One of the stony meteorites that fell in Moore County, North Carolina on April 21, 1913.

Notice the black shiny crust and the flow marks which seem to radiate from the apex of the stone. (*United States National Museum.*)

PIERCING THE ATMOSPHERE

When these bodies dash into the earth's atmosphere they are suddenly subjected to high temperatures and pressures. Because they move faster than air molecules, the air is trapped and greatly compressed in front of the cosmic plunger. Such a cap of compressed air becomes intensely hot and melts the surface material of the meteorite. In the air stream this liquid is continually swept away, the droplets appearing as sparks. These fireballs blaze into the lower part of the atmosphere producing intense detonations which from near by sound like the sharp crack of cannon fire while from afar they are like the distant roll of thunder. When the velocity of the meteorite has been greatly reduced through friction, the hot air-cap is no longer maintained, the fireball dies out and the liquid freezes into a dark crust. For stony material the crust is a real glass (Figure 71), but for the metallic stuffs it is of iron and nickel oxides as smooth as

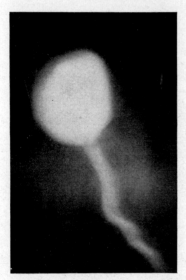

glass. Some meteorites are shaped like blunt cones with flow marks radiating from the apex while the flat base seems to have been protected from the air blast. Evidently these blocks kept the same side forward during the air flight and were carved into their conical form. The non-conical meteorites have a great variety of forms and probably spun over and over as they fell.

Under the high pressure of the compressed air cap stony meteorites shatter. Instead then of a single mass reaching the earth a great shower of particles of various sizes is sprayed over an area that covers many square kilometers. Thousands of fragments down to the size of a pea were collected from an area five kilometers long and one kilometer wide under the Holbrook, Arizona, meteor

Fig. 72.—The great meteor of March 24, 1933 as photographed by Mr. Charles M. Brown from Mount Dora, New Mexico.

As the meteor shot through the sky, Mr. Brown snatched his camera and snapped this remarkable picture. Farther along its path the meteor dropped many meteorites near Pasamonte, New Mexico.

of July 19, 1912. Customarily the long axis of such an area closely parallels the motion of the meteor and the largest masses lie at the end toward which the meteor moved. Iron meteorites sometimes fall in several pieces, but usually their toughness can withstand the hazards of flight through the atmosphere. In contrast, only rarely is a single stone collected that appears to constitute the total fall. Nininger

Fig. 73.—Excavation of the Hugoton, Kansas meteorite.

This great stony meteorite weighing 346 kilograms was discovered when a plow turned up a fragment. When excavated by Nininger, it proved to be one of the largest stony meteorites known. (*Photo by H. H. Nininger.*)

Fig. 74.—An excavated meteorite.

A metallic meteorite weighing over thirteen kilograms unearthed by LaPaz during the Ohio State University Meteorite Expedition of 1939. It was excavated from a depth of a meter after being located by use of an electric "divining rod". (*Lincoln LaPaz.*)

reports cases like the Pasamonte meteor of March 24, 1933, Figure 72 where for kilometers along under the path of a stony meteorite fine gravelly particles fell.

When a meteorite has been so retarded that the cap of hot air dissipates, the fireball vanishes and the dark body falls as though released from an airplane. Large meteorites strike the ground with such force that they bury themselves to considerable depths. The forty-three kilogram Hraschina iron plunged a meter into a recently plowed field. During ancient times many large meteorites, especially the irons,

Fig. 75.—Meteorites located in twelve hours of searching.

This collection of thirteen metallic meteorites was unearthed at the Odessa meteor crater after LaPaz had surveyed the region for only twelve hours using the meteorite detector of the Ohio State University Meteorite Expedition of 1939. (*Lincoln LaPaz.*)

buried themselves deeply into the soft subsoil and there they stayed until they disintegrated or the overlying material eroded away and a plow struck them (Figure 73). More than five per cent of discovered meteorites have been unearthed in the course of excavations, some lying as deep as six meters. Thus a vast number of undiscovered bodies must lie beneath our feet.

Various electrical and magnetic divining-rods for locating buried meteorites have been made and tested. One of the most effective was made by LaPaz and used in his survey of the Odessa meteor crater. With this device he located meteorites to depths exceeding a meter. The meteorites he located within twelve hours and excavated during a survey of this crater make the large collection shown in Figure 75.

Their Temperature

One general misconception regarding meteorites involves their temperatures both while in space and as they fall through the air. All bodies exposed to sunlight are warmed just as the earth and moon are. The presence of an atmosphere on the earth aids somewhat in retaining the heat, but at any solar distance, r, in astronomical units, the approximate absolute temperature of an atmosphereless mass can be computed from the relation:

$$T_r = \frac{277°}{\sqrt{r}}.$$

Since melting ice has a temperature of 273° on this scale, at the earth's distance from the sun meteorites have temperatures comparable to those of ordinary rocks.

As the bodies dash through the atmosphere their outer surfaces are intensely heated and liquefied. Under the terrific air blast to which they are exposed this liquid is immediately swept away and a fresh cool layer of material exposed. During the air flight, which lasts only a few minutes, the heat from the nearly liquid surface material has little opportunity to leak inward. Freshly fallen irons are generally just too hot to handle comfortably while stones are milk warm. Both materials cool quickly, thereby showing that the heat was only skin deep and that the meteorites remained at their pre-atmospheric temperature except for a thin crustal layer.

In no case has grass, hay or other inflammable material under a freshly fallen meteorite been charred or scorched. The reports that a meteorite was red-hot or glowing when found may be discounted and attributed to preconceptions.

THEIR NUMBER AND MASS

From the number of meteorites that fall within the central region of the United States we estimate that the total falling over this country is twenty-five each year. For the whole earth the number is two thousand per year, five or six per day. From more than four hundred falls the average mass collected is twenty kilograms, but a sizable portion of each meteorite must be lost when it passes through the atmosphere and by the scattering of fragments over a large area. To allow for this loss, we assume that the average weight of each meteorite was one hundred kilograms before it entered the atmosphere. Then the earth's total accretion of meteorites throughout a year is some two hundred tons, less than a ton per day.

LARGE METEORITES

The largest known meteorite, called Hoba West, is a roughly rectangular block weighing approximately sixty tons, three by three meters with a thickness varying from eight-tenths to one meter. It lies in limestone where it was found near Grootfontein, South West Africa. Surrounding the mass is a layer of laminated iron-shale that follows the contours of the meteorite; allowance for the metal in this shale brings the original mass to more than eighty tons. The meteorite is unusually rich in nickel, containing sixteen per cent, and is unusually malleable and difficult to cut. Two natives required two full days and a great quantity of hack-saw blades to cut a surface only eight by thirteen centimeters.

Second in size is Ahnighito (The Tent) weighing thirty-three tons which was brought from Cape York, Greenland in 1897 by Peary. He also brought to this country two other meteorites that lay nearby, The Woman of one and a half tons and The Dog of one half ton. The three masses are on exhibition at the Hayden Planetarium in New York City, while a fourth, Savik, is in Copenhagen. From these the

Fig. 76.—The Hoba West meteorite, largest known.

This sixty ton mass of metal lies where it was found in South West Africa.

Esquimos pounded off fragments of metal which they used as knives and spear tips.

The largest meteorite found in the United States and the fourth largest in the world, also on exhibition at the Hayden Planetarium, comes from near Willamette, Oregon. As this conical body of fourteen tons lay nose down in the moist forest the exposed upper surface was severely oxidized and great cavities formed. The original mass must have been twenty or twenty-five tons. The meteorite was discovered in 1902 on property belonging to the Oregon Iron and Steel

Company. The discoverer, who lived nearby, spent three months secretly at work in the forest moving the mass to his own property. Shortly after he began to exhibit it, the Oregon Iron and Steel Company filed suit to regain possession. Eventually the Supreme Court of Oregon ruled that it

Fig. 77.—The Ahnighito meteorite, largest in captivity.

Dr. Clyde Fisher, Honorary Curator of the Hayden Planetarium in New York, makes notes about the meteorite. It was found in Greenland and brought to New York by Peary in 1897. (*Thane L., Bierwert, American Museum of Natural History, New York.*)

belonged to the owner of the land on which it was found. In some countries meteorites belong to the government and in others it is "finders keepers."

Seven meteorites weighing a ton or more have been found in the uplands of Northern Mexico; at least one of the masses was known to the conquistadores. The largest of these bodies, Bacubirito, having an estimated mass of twenty-four tons, lies where it was unearthed in the state of Sinaloa. At Chupaderos in Chihuahua two masses of fourteen and six and a half tons lay a hundred meters apart. Their surface features dove-tail and indicate that they originally formed a single body. The fourth of these giant meteorites is Morito (El Morito) a beautiful conical mass of ten tons. The Chupaderos masses and Morito are on display in Mexico City.

Fig. 78.—The Willamette meteorite.

Its present weight is 14 tons, but before the deep erosion began the weight must have been near 25 tons. (*Julius Kirschner and Clyde Fisher, American Museum of Natural History, New York.*)

Metallic meteorites exceeding a ton have also been found in Tanganyika Territory, Africa; in Brazil; in Argentina and in Australia. Reports of exceedingly large meteorites appear from time to time but as yet they have not been verified. A body with the fabulous length of a hundred meters and height of twenty meters has been reported as near Chinguetti in the Adrar Desert, French West Africa. A small sample examined in Paris was meteoritic but the main mass has not been visited by a scientist and upon inspection, if it can ever be found, will probably prove to be much smaller than the reported dimensions.

METEOR CRATERS

Each year billions of tiny, millions of small, thousands of large and a few great bodies strike the earth. So far we have discussed only the characteristics of the small and moderate sized bodies. For the great masses the violence of the impact is terrific. A body several hundred meters in diameter, having a mass of many million tons, will pierce the earth's atmosphere without being appreciably checked and crash into the ground while moving fifteen to seventy kilometers a second. The holacaust that follows is difficult to describe in detail, but some effects are self evident in the form of meteor craters.

As the mass plunges into the ground its forward motion is checked in a minute fraction of a second. Through this braking action the outer parts of the meteorite and the contacting ground are tremendously compressed, heated and partly turned to vapor. This gas, with steam from the omnipresent ground water, expands in a terrific explosion blowing much of the meteorite back out of the ground, tearing a gaping crater. The meteorite is shattered and widely scattered over the surrounding area; at best a fraction of the original body remains in the crater. An intensely hot air blast spreads out burning and destroying nearby plant and animal life. Simultaneously strong earth-waves spread from the crater, warping and shattering the surrounding rock strata.

At the beginning of the twentieth century the Barringers and their associates suggested that the large crater in Arizona had a meteoric origin. Geologists were reluctant to accept this novel explanation and contended that the more familiar processes associated with volcanic action, steam blow-outs, or sinks were more probable. Gradually, however, indisputable evidence supporting the meteoric origin appeared and now this explanation is generally accepted. With the Arizona crater as an example geologists are alert for similar craters that defy explanation by the common geological processes. In no case, however, is the meteoric explanation acceptable until all the ordinary crater forming-processes have been eliminated or unmistakable meteoritic evidence is found.

In Table 23 we summarize our present knowledge of meteor craters; there are ten craters or groups of craters unquestionably of meteoric origin. Similar origin has been suggested for other craters, but as yet the evidence is inconclusive. In the following pages we shall explore the salient features of these craters to see how they reveal the process of formation.

TABLE 23
METEOR CRATERS

Name	Number	Diameter,* meters	Date of discovery	Meteorites
Arizona..........	1	1200	1891	Yes
Odessa..........	1	170	1921	Yes
Brenham.........	1	17	1933	Yes
Campo del Cielo..	Many	75	?	Yes
Henbury.........	13	200 × 110	1931	Yes
Boxhole..........	1	175	1937	Yes
Dalgaranga.......	1	70	1923	Yes
Wabar..........	2	100	1932	Yes
Ösel............	6	100	1927	Fragments
Siberia..........	10 or more	50	1908–23	Microscopic fragments

* Largest crater when there are several.

Arizona Crater

The Arizona Meteor Crater, the largest known, is situated between Winslow and Flagstaff in a large level plateau of stratified limestone and sandstone. It is nearly circular and averages 1200 meters across. The rim stands thirty-seven meters above the surrounding plain while the present depth is 175 meters from the rim to the crater floor. Many rocks in and around the crater are mute evidence of

Fig. 79.—The Arizona Meteor Crater.

The great crater, more than a kilometer wide, as photographed from an altitude of 2000 feet. Note the up-turned rim. (*Photo by Clyde Fisher.*)

the crushing impact. Tons of pulverized sandstone comprise a fine rock-flour both under the crater floor and around the rim. Other sandstone fragments show evidence of melting, being fused and spongy, sometimes including particles of nickel-iron. Still other fragments reveal how the original horizontal bandings in the rocks were warped and twisted by the blow. To a distance of several kilometers from the crater thousands of metallic meteorites weighing from a few grams to 500 kilograms lay intermingled with rock fragments. Enthusiastic collectors have already removed nearly all the meteoritic material and at present a sample can rarely be found on the surface. With electrical and magnetic detecting devices sizable chunks are now being located and excavated from depths of two to three meters. A few more years of such gleaning will completely strip this region of meteorites. Throughout all the investigations no meteorite of any size has been found inside the crater. Some small exposed meteorites have been completely oxidized and now

Fig. 80.—The west rim of the Meteor Crater.

This photograph shows the sharply up-turned rocks in the rim and the great quantity of fragmental material lying about. (*Lincoln LaPaz.*)

constitute shale balls, while others are partly oxidized but contain metallic cores.

During the earliest investigations the circular shape misled the Barringers into the assumption that the meteorite fell vertically. Numerous drill holes through the crater floor passed through a few hundred meters of pulverized and shattered rock containing small metallic particles and then into relatively undisturbed layers. The lack of meteoritic material under the crater and the undisturbed condition of the deep underlying strata were a great puzzle. Finally several clues gave the correct answer. Barringer noticed that rifle bullets striking mud at a large angle make not elliptical but circular holes. Then he saw that the exposed strata in the crater rim have been tilted upward and sloped away from the center. In the northern rim this tilt is only five

Fig. 81.—Inside the Meteor Crater.

The inner structure of the crater as seen from the northwest rim, the opposite crater walls show up-tilted strata and, at the right, the great arch raised vertically. On the floor of the crater, 175 meters below the rim, are the remains of the old drilling machinery used in the early surveys of the crater structure. (*Photo by Clyde Fisher.*)

degrees, but it steadily increases around the eastern and western walls until in the southeast and southwest the exposed strata are nearly vertical. Across the southern rim a broad arch, 800 meters long, has been raised vertically thirty-two meters. These peculiarities suggest that the meteor struck from the north at a considerable angle and penetrated under the southern rim. Once this possibility was clear, the earlier drill holes gave supporting evidence, for those through the southern part of the crater floor went deepest before encountering undisturbed rocks. A churn drill was driven down through the southern rim of the crater. Below 365 meters it passed through a region increasingly rich in meteoritic material and at 410 meters

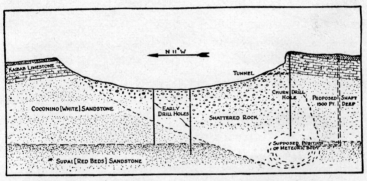

Fig. 82.—Cross-section of the Arizona Meteor Crater.

The rocks under the crater are shattered but lie much as they did before the impact of the meteor crushed them. (*Scientific American.*)

struck a region containing seventy-five per cent nickel-iron which was exceedingly resistant to boring. After passing through ten meters of this material the drill finally stuck and remains today immovable. Recent electrical and magnetic surveys of the region around the crater suggest that a sizable amount of metallic material lies under the southern rim, but estimates of the amount and location vary.

No one knows how long ago this crater was formed. We can only estimate from the rate at which it is eroded and from the rate at which the meteorites rust away forming shale balls of sand grains cemented together by iron oxides. Certainly the crater had no recent origin; many estimates put the origin back five thousand years but even seventy-five thousand years is not an impossible interval since the day it was blasted in this arid plateau.

OTHER AMERICAN CRATERS

Two other meteor craters are found in the United States. Near Odessa, in western Texas, a crater roughly 170 meters in diameter and five meters deep was discovered in 1921.

Fig. 83.— The Odessa Crater.

A view of the shallow crater and its rim composed of up-turned rock fragments. (*Lincoln LaPaz.*)

Several small meteorites and shale-balls were found there and recently Nininger has dragged this region with a magnetic plow collecting 1500 metallic fragments. Where the rock strata are visible in the crater rim, they slope away from the center at angles of twenty to thirty degrees. The eroded condition of the crater and the weathered state of the meteoritic fragments indicate a great age for the crater.

Near Brenham, Kansas, fragments of stony-iron meteorites were discovered in 1885 and from an area of several square kilometers nearly a ton of material was collected during the next few years. In 1933 Nininger began excavating a previously unnoticed buffalo wallow. It proved to be a meteor crater seventeen by eleven meters across and about three meters deep; the long dimension lies along a line WNW to ESE. Within the crater he found several meteorites weighing up to twenty-six kilograms and hundreds of small partly oxidized fragments.

At Campo del Cielo in the Grand Chaco of Argentina are a number of round shallow depressions, the largest being seventy-five meters in diameter with a rim rising one meter above the surrounding pampa. Nearby lay a number of meteorites with masses exceeding a ton. Recently one of the depressions, fifty-three meters in diameter and five meters deep was partially excavated. Underneath were "white ash," "transparent glass" and small fragments of meteoritic iron. The "ash" and "glass" were similar to the rock-flour and fused silica found at the Arizona Crater. Further investigation of these depressions should be made as soon as possible for they may prove to be the world's largest group of meteor craters.

Australian Craters

In 1931 a group of thirteen craters and much meteoritic iron was found in central Australia, near Henbury. Alderman, who investigated the region, showed conclusively that the craters were of meteoritic origin. Twelve of the craters are roughly circular with diameters ranging between nine and eighty meters. The largest crater is oval with dimensions of 200 and 110 meters, and twelve to fifteen meters deep; apparently it was formed by the overlapping of two adjacent craters. In the smallest of the craters, the one nine meters across, four fragments of meteoritic iron, the weathered remains of a single mass weighing 200 kilograms, were found three meters below the ground level. In the

Fig. 84.—The Main Crater at Henbury.

In the center of Australia are a group of thirteen meteor craters
of which this is the largest, 200 meters long and 110 meters wide.
(*Photograph by A. R. Alderman, from his article in the Mineralogical Magazine.*)

formation of this small crater the energy generated was
not sufficient to completely shatter and back-fire the intrud-
ing mass.

The metal collected around the Henbury craters contains
7.3 per cent nickel and shows the crystal pattern peculiar to
meteorites. In the smallest fragments, some of which are
twisted slugs, this pattern has been partially destroyed,
evidence that they have been momentarily heated to at
least 850°C. These craters are in a semi-arid region like the
plateau of Arizona and their eroded condition suggests an
age comparable to that of the Arizona crater. Yet the natives
fear the region and speak of it as "chindu chinna waru
chingi yabu" or "sun walk fire devil rock." This sounds like
a cryptic description of the meteor and crater-forming
explosion, which poses an interesting question for sociolo-
gists—how long will primitive peoples transmit legends and
taboos?

Recently two additional meteor craters have been discovered in Australia. At Boxhole about 300 kilometers NE
of Henbury is a crater 175 meters across, ten to sixteen
meters deep with a rim three to five meters high. The crater

is weatherbeaten and probably quite old. Nearby were shale-balls and fragments of meteoritic metal and a meteorite of eighty-two kilograms. *

Near Dalgaranga a crater seventy meters wide and five meters deep was discovered in 1923. Around its rim, especially on the northwest side, sizable rock fragments have been tilted up. In the vicinity were many fragments of meteoritic iron having a bent and confused structure like that of the small pieces found at Henbury. †

ARABIAN AND ESTONIAN CRATERS

Far from Australia, in the Great South Desert of Arabia are two unusual meteor craters. Both are hardly more than depressions in the desert; the larger is nearly circular with a diameter of one hundred meters and a depth of twelve meters, the smaller is fifty-five by forty meters. The shifting desert sands have nearly concealed the deep pits and shattered structure in the underlying rock. Near-by lay several pieces of meteoric iron and numerous masses of frozen silica foam containing shiny metallic globules. Spencer, formerly Keeper of the Minerals in the British Museum, concluded that these tiny spheres flew through an atmosphere from which oxygen had momentarily been eliminated and were trapped in the boiling sand. Not only was the sand liquefied, but it was even vaporized for the surfaces of the glassy chunks show dew-like drops of condensed silica. Some idea of the temperature developed in the explosion may be obtained from the geological thermometer given by Spencer:

---

* C. T. Madigan, Trans. R. Soc. So. Australia, *61*, 187, 1937. The position of the crater is given as 22° 37′ S, 135° 12′ E.

† E. S. Simpson, Min. Mag., *25*, 157, 1938. The position of this crater is given as 27° 45′ S, 117° 05′ E.

	Degrees Centigrade
Iron melts............................	1535
Silica melts..........................	1710
Iron boils............................	2900
Silica boils..........................	3500

Far to the north on the Estonian Island of Ösel, there are six craters of which the largest is nearly circular with a

Fig. 85.—Silica-glass from Wabar, Arabia.

The broken surface of a silica bomb shows patches of white glass and large bubbles embedded in grey and blue glass. This silica-foam contains many minute spherules of shiny nickel-iron. (*Photo. from the Mineralogical Magazine.*)

diameter of one hundred meters and a rim six meters above ground level. Rock powder and fragments appear in the rim and under the crater. Since this crater is occupied by a lake its thorough study is impossible, but in nearly every feature it is a miniature of the Arizona crater. Of the five other craters four are circular, approximately thirty-five, thirty-three, twenty and ten meters across. The fifth is oval, fifty-three by thirty-six meters but deeper at one end; it probably was formed from two over-lapping circular depressions. Reinwaldt, Inspector for the Mining Industry of Estonia, has

Fig. 86.—Aerial view of the craters at Ösel.

An aerial photograph by the Estonian Air Defense shows the main crater, K.j., and the location of six other small craters. The main crater is occupied by a lake and cannot be thoroughly studied, but Reinwaldt has excavated the small crater numbered 5.

extensively studied the craters since 1927 by cutting trenches across them and by completely excavating the small crater twenty meters wide. In all cases the results were similar: the limestone strata comprising the walls have been raised and slope away from the center at angles of thirty to forty degrees. In the jagged edges of the upturned strata are large quantities of pulverized rock, while below lie strata in their normal horizontal position. In the rock below the center of the excavated crater Reinwaldt found a short funnel a meter wide and a half meter deep. The adjacent limestone is cracked and has a burnt appearance.

Fig. 87.—The foot-print of a meteorite.

Reinwaldt examines the funnel-shaped depression he found under a small meteor crater on the Ösel Islands in the Baltic Sea. (*Photo. by Clyde Fisher.*)

After ten years of effort Reinwaldt in 1937 found conclusive proof of the meteoritic origin of these craters in the form of twenty-eight small fragments of meteoritic iron totaling 110 grams. That large masses are not found now is not surprising, for the islands have been inhabited and tilled for centuries and any sizable metallic masses were probably removed long ago.

SIBERIAN CRATERS

On the morning of June 30, 1908 (at 0h 16m Greenwich Civil Time) a great meteor blazed northward over central Siberia and crashed to the earth in an isolated region near the Stony Tunguska River. The resulting explosion was so tremendous that windows were broken eighty kilometers away while 700 kilometers away on the Trans-Siberian

Fig. 88.—Destruction near the Siberian Meteor Crater.

Over an area nearly a hundred kilometers across the trees were pushed over by the great blast of hot air that shot out when the meteor struck the earth.

Railway an engineer stopped his train for fear it would be derailed. For many years the rumors about this great meteor received no scientific attention, but finally in 1923 a Russian scientist, Kulik, began collecting reports. In 1927 he led an expedition to the region and near latitude 61° N longitude 102° E found a great area of devastation centered around at least ten craters ranging from ten to fifty meters across. Other expeditions went to the highly inaccessible region where the ground is frozen all winter and turns to

Fig. 89.—One of the Siberian Craters.

Located in a marshy region of central Siberia these craters are very difficult to study.

marsh with the thaws; in 1930–31 Kulik established a camp here and explored the craters for thirteen months. Under one crater he found rock-flour and fused quartz containing minute grains of nickel-iron.

Around the craters the devastation is frightful. Over a small central area tree trunks stand vertically, stripped of their branches and seared by fire. Out to a distance of thirty kilometers all the trees have been blown over and lie along lines radiating from the craters. Even at distances of sixty to ninety kilometers the effects of the blast are apparent. Accompanying the explosion a great pillar of smoke shot up at least twenty kilometers into the atmosphere. On the nights following the fall European observers noted especially beautiful twilights and what seemed to be very high cirrus clouds. These probably were caused by dust and smoke that spread through the upper atmosphere from the explosion. If this meteorite had met the earth just four hours and forty-seven minutes later, we should have known of the blast much sooner, for it would have scored a bull's-eye hit upon the city of St. Petersburg, now called Leningrad.

The explosion wave spread out causing deviations in the barographic records at many Siberian stations. Five hours after the impact the air wave reached England, 5500 kilometers from the fall point. Not only was an air wave observed, but European seismographs recorded a strong ground wave. From the energy liberated in these waves and in the destruction at the fall-point the mass of the meteorites is estimated as a few hundred tons, comparable to a locomotive. The destruction caused by this meteor seems tremendous, yet the craters formed are among the smallest known. These depressions in a marsh and decimated forest will disappear in a few hundred years and nothing will remain to indicate their former existence.

METEOR CRATERS IN GENERAL

From the ten meteor craters or groups of craters mentioned we can see that the outstanding characteristics of meteor craters are: nearly circular shape; rims tilted up so they slope away from the center; the presence of meteoritic material nearby. If the place of impact contains sand or sandstone, chunks of frozen silica will be formed by the liquefication and vaporization of the sand. The material surrounding and lying under the crater is always bent and warped by the force of the impact. The small excavated craters at Henbury, Brenham and Ösel illustrate the transition between the splashed or gouged pits made by small meteorites and the large explosion craters. At Henbury in the crater nine meters wide a large mass of metal lay in the crater. The larger Brenham Crater contained numerous fragments whose size increased with depth, but no single large mass. At Ösel the crater twenty meters across contained no meteoritic material, but a scar reveals the point at which the explosive forces were concentrated. Larger craters are all formed on the same pattern having circular shapes and up-turned rims. The multiplicity of craters at five of the ten locations must mean that small swarms of metallic bodies move through space.

At present only a few widely separated and relatively inaccessible meteor craters are known; but since their reality has been admitted for only a few decades, many similar depressions doubtless await discovery. Few of these will be near cities because cities frequent areas of high rainfall where craters are rapidly obliterated by erosion. Furthermore the intensive cultivation that generally surrounds cities also acts as an eraser. From the number of craters known we can estimate that meteorites capable of producing craters ten or more meters in diameter strike the earth once each century.

FOSSIL CRATERS AND LUNAR CRATERS

Fossil meteor craters, the remnants of great ancient craters, may, according to the discussions of Boon and Albritton, dot the earth. They point out how during great intervals of time erosion will remove the rocks surrounding the upper portions of a crater and expose the underlying folded and shattered strata. In the south and west of the United States are circular structures several kilometers across that exhibit bilateral symmetry, central uplifts, and extremely pulverized rocks. Although these are generally attributed to the explosion of volcanic gases, geologists find little evidence for intense volcanic activity during the era when these depressions were formed. A meteor crater several kilometers across would be formed if the earth collided with one of the closely-approaching asteroids. The fossil craters may be the eroded marks of such collisions in the long past. Until we know more about the deep underlying structure of large meteor craters we shall not be certain how the fossil craters were formed.

If great meteorites are blasting craters in the earth, they must be doing the same on the moon, which lacks any

Fig. 90.—The rim of the Arizona Meteor Crater.

Seen from a distance of several kilometers the crater resembles the numerous craters on the moon. (*Photo. by Clyde Fisher.*)

protecting atmosphere. The surface of our satellite is well pitted with yawning craters, the largest are 150 kilometers across while thousands exceed the size of the Arizona Meteor Crater. Although we are sure that millions of meteors strike the moon each day, there is no conclusive proof that any observable change in lunar topography has occurred within the past century. While it has been suggested that the lunar craters resulted from meteoric bombardment, many astronomers favor the theory of a volcanic origin.*

* See Chapter 9 of *Whipple, Earth, Moon and Planets.*

9

METEORITES
IN THE LABORATORY

IN 1803, AFTER YEARS OF SKEPTICISM, THE FRENCH
Academy, representing the scientific world, officially
acknowledged that stones could and did fall to the earth
from surrounding space. Previously, dark stones found after
"thunderstorms," some of which occurred under cloudless
skies, were attributed to the action of lightning upon ac-
cumulations of dust in the atmosphere or upon ordinary
rocks. At the end of the eighteenth century Chladni was
convinced that meteorites originated somewhere off the
earth and he was supported in this conclusion by the
researches of Brandes and Benzenberg about ordinary meteors. But it remained for Biot to make such a thorough investigation of the fall of stones at L'Aigle, France, April 26,
1803, that the most sceptical academician was silenced and
the scientific world acknowledged the existence of meteorites.
An extramundane origin was, however, not immediately
accepted everywhere by the general populace. Upon hear-
ing of a stone that fell from the sky at Weston, Connecticut
on December 17, 1807, Thomas Jefferson, then President

of the United States, reputedly said, "I could more easily believe that two Yankee professors would lie than that stones would fall from heaven." Even now some people may be of the same opinion.

Here, at last, in the meteorites we have some of the interplanetary material which we can handle, scrutinize, analyse and test with every device in the laboratory. What meteorites are and how they are put together seems a matter that should have been settled long ago. But we are still far from having the complete answer. Their study requires the comprehensive and coöperative work of many types of scientists—mineralogists, metallurgists, chemists, petrologists, physicists and astronomers—each of whom uses his own technical terms. During the nineteenth century many capable mineralogists and chemists accumulated isolated facts about the mineralogical and chem-

Fig. 91.—The Carlton meteorite.

A surface of this metallic meteorite polished and etched in dilute acid shows this beautiful pattern known as the Widmanstätten figure. As yet it has not been duplicated in similar man-made alloys. (*Photo. by Thane L. Bierwert, American Museum of Natural History, New York.*)

ical structure of meteorites, but could form no coherent and consistent explanation for what they observed. They needed the advice and assistance of other scientists, for the findings in each subject limit the possible explanations to be drawn from the others. Recently interest in meteorites has revived and the use of new techniques: microchemical analysis, crystal examination with X-rays and studies with the mass-spectrograph offer the possibility of gaining the fundamental information necessary for a new attempt to account for these strange and complex bodies.

We all wonder if meteorites are like asteroids. The only way by which we may compare meteorites with the distant and inaccessible asteroids is through the effects they produce upon the light they reflect. Of fifty stony meteorites examined to see whether or not they colored light upon reflection all but one made it just slightly redder. The reflectivities of these stony meteorites range from five per cent for the blackest to fifty per cent for the whitest. One metallic meteorite was tested and found to have a color and reflectivity indistinguishable from those of a typical stone; if asteroids are similar we would not be able to distinguish one that is metallic from one that is stony. The colors and reflectivities of meteorites compare well with those of the asteroids and the two types of material may be similar, but many terrestrial materials also have colors and reflectivities like those of asteroids.

CHEMICAL COMPOSITION

In his laboratory the chemist can soon determine which chemical elements are abundant in meteorites and in what quantities. But when he begins searching for minute traces of some his troubles increase rapidly. Thus it was long rumored that gold and silver existed in meteorites, but the precious metals were found in the metallic meteorites only through painstaking work, for their total quantity averages but sixty grams in a ton. Measurement of the radioactive elements—radium, uranium and thorium—was even more difficult. In the metallic meteorites the total uranium and thorium runs a tenth of a gram to the ton, but in the stony meteorites they are about six times more abundant. For comparison we note that the average ton of granite contains twenty grams of the radioactive elements.

Taking many meteorites we find the average compositions in Table 24. Compared to the earth's crust the stony meteorites are deficient in oxygen and silicon so we cannot expect to find the same compounds and minerals in meteorites and the average terrestrial rock.

TABLE 24

COMPOSITION OF METEORITES AND OF THE EARTH'S CRUST

Irons		*Stones*		*Earth's crust*
Iron	90.8%	Oxygen	36.3%	49.4%
Nickel	8.5	Iron	25.6	4.7
Cobalt	0.59	Silicon	18.0	25.8
Phosphorus	0.17	Magnesium	14.2	1.9
Sulphur	0.04	Aluminium	1.5	7.5
Carbon	0.03	Nickel	1.4	0.02
Copper	0.02	Calcium	1.3	3.4
Chromium	0.01	Sodium	0.6	2.6
		Chromium	0.27	0.03
		Phosphorus	0.19	0.12
		Manganese	0.18	0.08
		Cobalt	0.14	
		Potassium	0.13	2.4
		Titanium	0.10	0.58

But averages such as those in Table 24 mask the diversity we find in various individual meteorites. In metallic meteorites the nickel content varies from five to nearly twenty per cent. Fortunately none of the terrestrial nickel-iron alloys have nickel contents within this range so the quantity of nickel in a piece of nickel-iron is a good test of whether or not it is a meteorite. The silica content of meteoric stones varies between thirty and fifty-five per cent and produces a corresponding diversity in their mineralogical structure. Table 25 shows other variations in their chemical composition. Some of the irregularities are interrelated, for example the abundance of magnesium varies inversely with that of calcium and aluminium. In Chapter 6 we have already seen how the varying abundances of calcium and magnesium affect the spectra of fireballs.

TABLE 25

VARIATIONS IN ABUNDANCE OF SOME ELEMENTS IN STONY METEORITES

Oxide........	Al_2O_3	MgO	CaO	Na_2O	Fe + FeO
Maximum....	13.50	35.80	24.51	3.96	33.95
Minimum.....	0.10	7.14	0.00	0.00	1.74
Average......	2.86	23.66	1.88	0.87	25.95

We may ask the chemist to derive an average composition for all meteorites, but he declines and points out that the average composition depends upon the relative quantity of stone and metal that fall. This is a problem for the astronomer and the meteorite-collector. Stony falls usually consist of many fragments scattered over a wide area. If one piece is seen to fall, a search reveals other pieces that increase the total recorded weight. In contrast, the tougher irons rarely split, the whole mass must be observed to fall or the event passes unrecorded. Through disruption and the wide scattering of fragments the number of stony meteorites seen to fall is disproportionally increased, but through this same scattering many fragments are lost; as a result the quantity of stony material collected per fall is much less than the quantity actually reaching the ground. Thus we find 392 stony falls yield 7705 kilograms while 21 iron falls yield 730 kilograms. The total material for stony falls is ten times greater than for irons, but the average iron gives nearly twice as much material as the average stone. These un-

TABLE 26
MEAN COMPOSITION OF METEORITES

Element	Ratio of stones to irons	
	4:1, per cent	*9:1,* per cent
Carbon.........................	0.14	0.15
Oxygen.........................	29.00	32.70
Sodium.........................	0.24	0.27
Magnesium......................	11.00	12.88
Aluminium......................	0.61	0.68
Silicon.........................	14.40	16.28
Phosphorus.....................	0.11	0.10
Sulphur.........................	1.90	1.87
Chlorine........................	0.02	.03
Potassium.......................	0.06	.06
Calcium.........................	1.10	1.18
Titanium........................	0.08	.09
Chromium.......................	0.12	.12
Manganese......................	0.15	.16
Iron............................	38.00	31.85
Cobalt..........................	0.22	0.18
Nickel..........................	2.80	2.08
Copper.........................	0.02	0.01

certainties prohibit an exact statement of the true proportions of falling stone and iron, but suggest that the stony material is from four to nine times more abundant than the metallic. Table 26 includes the average composition computed for these proportions.

In calculating this table we have assumed that our museums contain a true sample of the various materials striking the atmosphere. But we may be mistaken. The meteorites that fell at Hessle, Sweden, on January 1, 1869 suggest as much. Associated with these typical stones was a quantity of coffee-colored, carbonaceous material containing metallic grains. When these were extracted the residue consisted chiefly of carbon, oxygen, silicon, and hydrogen. The like of this material has never again been seen and its significance remains a mystery.

When a meteorite is pulverized and heated small quantities of gas appear. In general metallic meteorites liberate hydrogen (H_2) and carbon-monoxide (CO) most abundantly while carbon-dioxide (CO_2), nitrogen (N_2) and methane (CH_4) are present in small quantities. In contrast stony meteorites liberate much carbon-dioxide with some hydrogen and traces of carbon-monoxide, nitrogen and methane. These are the gases observed in comets and we are tempted to identify meteorites with the solid bodies of a comet's nucleus; yet we lack a meteorite from a meteor shower to complete the chain of evidence.

Since meteorites come from out in space, they may have originated where the chemical elements differed from those on the earth. We ask the physicist to check this by examining the abundances of isotopes—atoms having differing weights but identical chemical properties, like light and heavy hydrogen. In many terrestrial materials the relative abundance of isotopes has been found to be constant. Seven elements: carbon, oxygen, silicon, chlorine, iron, nickel and cobalt, have been taken from meteorites and tested. In no case did their isotopic abundances differ significantly from those of terrestrial materials. At present we do not know whether this means that the earth and the meteorites originally came from the same material, possibly the sun, or whether throughout the universe the relative abundances of isotopes remain constant.

Fig. 92.—The Goose-Lake Meteorite.

On October 13, 1938 a party of hunters discovered this mass lying on the lava beds of northeastern California. It is the fourth-largest meteorite found in the United States, weighing 1167 kilograms. It was recovered by E. G. Linsley and other members of the Society for Research on Meteorites.

Chemical Compounds

We can learn much about the origin of meteorites by noting how the atoms are joined together as compounds. Recent investigations with X-rays, which can penetrate and reveal the innermost arrangements of molecules, show that in the metallic alloy the nickel and iron do not form a chemical compound, for their atoms are not arranged with the required regularity. Included within the nickel-iron are, however, a number of compounds. The most abundant is iron-sulphide, called troilite, which appears in a variety of shapes, most frequently as rough spheroids or as bands.

Troilite weathers away rapidly and as it disintegrates great cavities grow like those in the recently-found Goose Lake meteorite (Figure 92). Phosphorus occurs in a complex compound of iron, nickel and cobalt called schreibersite found only in meteorites. Schreibersite is brittle, white and strongly magnetic and occurs in several forms, most fre-

Fig. 93.—Internal structure of the Hex River Meteorite.

Magnified sixty times this meteorite, of the hexahedrite class, shows large schreibersite needles and an irregular inclusion of troilite. (*Stuart H. Perry.*)

quently as needles (Figure 93). Carbon is combined with the metallic atoms as cohenite; it also occurs free in both the amorphous form—large graphite nodules in the irons of coarsest structure—and in the crystalline form as microscopic diamonds. Although their commercial value is nil and they enhance the difficulties of properly polishing the materials in which they occur, the presence of diamonds is an important clue to the past history of meteorites because, although the origin of terrestrial diamonds is not clearly understood, high temperatures and pressures were probably involved in their formation. One compound seldom present in any quantity, but often present in traces, is a metallic chloride, lawrencite, which hastens the rusting and decomposition of meteorites. The great three-ton Cranbourne meteorite from Australia has been rusting so rapidly that recently it was placed in a special nitrogen-filled case.

The chemical compounds found in stony meteorites are chiefly complex silicates similar to those in volcanic lavas. For all silicates the fundamental unit is the tetrahedron of four oxygen atoms around a single silicon atom. In this compact group the silicon atom fits snugly into the central space, which accounts for the chemical and physical stability of the silicates, as, for example, their insolubility and high melting points. These tetrahedra may join in various ways to produce numerous compounds: as plates to form mica, in chains to form asbestos, or in networks of varying tightness. In each of the various silica families the number of atoms is constant, the pyroxenes containing ten atoms and the feldspars thirteen. Aluminium atoms occasionally replace some but apparently never more than half of the silicon atoms. When aluminium having three electrical charges does replace silicon having four, other atomic changes must also occur to keep the molecule electrically neutral while preserving the number of atoms. Thus between the related feldspars albite, $KAlSi_3O_8$, and anorthite, $CaAl_2Si_2O_8$, the replacement of one silicon atom by aluminium involves the replacement of monovalent potassium by bivalent calcium. Many changes of this type are possible within each of the silicate families and they produce a huge variety of silicate minerals.

The most common mineral in stony meteorites is the magnesium-iron silicate, olivine* $(Mg, Fe)_2SiO_4$. This molecule of seven tightly-packed atoms forms a dense mineral. Second in abundance are the orthorhombic pyroxenes, $(Mg, Fe)_2Si_2O_6$; three forms are generally recognized: magnesium-rich enstatite of a light hue; bronzite of intermediate hue and magnesium content; and dark, iron-rich hypersthene. Monoclinic pyroxenes appear generally as minor constituents, in the form of augite, $Ca(Mg, Fe, Al) (Al, Si)_2O_6$. Feldspars, which comprise sixty per cent of igneous rocks, are generally found in the form of anorthite, $CaAl_2Si_2O_8$. Other compounds occasionally found include calcium-sulphide, called oldhamite, a compound not found terrestrially, troilite and lawrencite. Conspicuously absent are water, quartz, mica and hornblend—prevalent constituents of the earth's crust.

Internal Structure of the Irons

After finding what the chemist can tell us about meteorites, we take them to the metallurgist who has a variety of tools and tests to use on them. When metallic meteorites are cut, polished and etched with dilute acid a pattern of intersecting bands, called the Widmanstätten figure, usually appears. It consists of three portions: wide bands or lamellae of nickel-poor kamacite, narrow bounding bands of shiny nickel-rich taenite, and the areas between lamellae filled with plessite, a mixture of kamacite and taenite. The lamellae parallel the faces of an octahedron, hence the meteorites in which they appear are called octahedrites and are sub-divided according to the width of the kamacite lamellae. O. C. Farrington of the Field Museum in Chicago

* By the bracket $(Mg, Fe)_2$ we mean that the two atoms may be magnesium or iron in any proportion.

found, Table 27, that as the kamacite lamellae became narrower the average iron content decreased.

Some meteorites do not show the Widmanstätten figure; those containing less than six or more than twelve per cent nickel have no extensive pattern and are termed respec-

Fig. 94.—Internal structure of the Wood's Mountain meteorite.

Magnified eighty-three times this octahedrite shows wide bands of granulated kamacite bounded by narrow taenite bands. The black areas are plessite having a variety of appearance and structure. (*Stuart H. Perry.*)

tively the nickel-poor and the nickel-rich ataxites. Among the nickel-poor ataxites are a sub-group which upon etching show fine lines, like scratches. These meteorites are the hexahedrites.

Any alloy showing a pattern like the Widmanstätten figures must consist of two crystal phases or types of metal, in this case kamacite and taenite. Each phase consists of

minute grains or blocks of a few thousand atoms arranged
according to a certain pattern. But no over-all pattern
would appear upon the meteorite when etched unless
similar grains were lined up over several centimeters.
The metallurgist tells us that the directions in which the
lamellae run mark the faces of an ancient crystal that

TABLE 27
STRUCTURE AND IRON CONTENT OF METALLIC METEORITES

	Abbreviation	Iron, per cent
Hexahedrites.........................	Hex	94.12
Coarsest Octahedrites.................	Ogg	93.18
Coarse Octahedrites..................	Og	92.28
Medium Octahedrites.................	Om	90.64
Fine Octahedrites....................	Of	90.18
Finest Octahedrites..................	Off	88.51

existed when the material had a temperature near 1000°C.
Since the Widmanstätten pattern often extends unbroken
for ten or more centimeters, these high-temperature crystals
must have been very large. But large crystals grow slowly,
especially in metal, so we conclude that during a great
interval, at least thousands of years, the atoms of the metal
were slowly linking arms and lining up to form the large
crystals. A few meteorites originally consisted of more than
one crystal, for Figure 95 shows a slice having six different
patterns each marking a former crystal.

Metallurgists probing by means of their furnaces, micro-
scopes and X-rays study how the atoms of alloys behave and
form new phases as their temperatures change. Our present
knowledge about nickel-iron is summarized in Figure 96.
In view of the great size of the crystals that existed in
meteorites, it is surprising to find that nickel-iron is a very
sluggish alloy extremely difficult to study in the laboratory.

Fig. 95.—Section of a Bethany meteorite.

This meteorite, one of more than fifty found close together in South Africa, shows several sets of Widmanstätten figures. Each marks a single crystal that existed in the meteorite when it had a temperature near 1000°C.

As a result our knowledge of how the nickel and iron atoms behave under various circumstances is still not complete, but the general picture seems clear. As a liquid mixture of nickel and iron cools and solidifies at 1500°C., the atoms form little grains or minute crystals. Because these show some propensity to line up parallel they gradually build up large crystals. As the temperature falls the high-temperature grains begin to break up and form two new grains or phases. One of these contains little nickel; if excess nickel is present, it is forced from this material to form a second phase rich in nickel. We identify the two types of grains with the kamacite containing six per cent nickel and the taenite containing about forty per cent. Since they have different

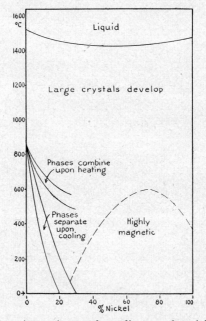

Fig. 96.—Approximate phase-diagram for nickel-iron.

This diagram shows how nickel-iron alloys of various compositions behave as their temperatures are changed. After solidifying from a liquid the nickel and iron tend to separate into two types of material, one rich in iron and the other rich in nickel.

solubilities in acid, their locations are revealed by etching. X-rays show that nickel-poor ataxites and hexahedrites containing less than six per cent nickel consist only of kamacite, while the nickel-rich ataxites contain considerable kamacite, but not enough to form lamellae.

This separation, or phase change, takes place within the solid material; the new grains align themselves parallel to the grains of the high-temperature crystal and preserve its original pattern, much as a piece of petrified wood retains the tree ring pattern. We can easily destroy the Widmanstätten figure by roasting the metal at a temperature of 800°C.; upon cooling only a granular structure remains. As yet the Widmanstätten pattern has not been artificially produced in metal similar in composition to meteorites, although such patterns occur frequently in other alloys—the strength of steel comes from the formation of similar strong crystals.

The high degree of organization present within metallic meteorites, where the nickel-iron crystals are oriented over large areas and even the inclusions of troilite, schreibersite and cohenite have definite crystal forms, can only mean that this material was once liquid. Subsequently it cooled at a very slow rate, presumably while insulated deep within some large body.

The crystal development we have suggested is probably correct, but we must remember that the pattern is never perfect, irregularities are frequent and, according to the X-ray analysis, the individual grains are sometimes out of alignment. Furthermore we have used pure nickel-iron for comparison while meteorites contain sulphur, phosphorus and carbon which may influence the behavior of the nickel-iron as it cools. Yet the greater part of these impurities has been expelled from the nickel-iron to form separate crystals or nodules of cohenite, schreibersite and troilite, as though the structure of the nickel-iron developed independently.

Moreover, the recent environment of the meteorites may have had some influence on their structure. For ages they have been separate bodies moving through space, attaining temperatures as low as liquid air when as far from the sun as Jupiter. A few experiments indicate that at such low temperatures the proportion of kamacite over taenite is increased and does not revert to the former state when warmed to room temperature. Recently Bradley and others have suggested that the Widmanstätten figures developed as the result of intermittent heating to 550°C. To attain this temperature a meteorite must pass the sun at scarcely more than 0.1 A.U. Undoubtedly some do pass this close, but the Widmanstätten pattern occurs in nearly every block of metal having the proper chemical composition whether in a large metallic mass or a stony-iron. It is not very probable that every mass passed so close to the sun and we must doubt that the Widmanstätten pattern was formed by recurrent heating.

INTERNAL STRUCTURE OF STONES

The stony meteorites present an extremely complex structure difficult to interpret. Under the microscope they show such a hodge-podge of fragmental and discolored crystals that the mineralogist has great trouble in identifying even the most common. Usually intermingled with the silicate material are numerous small inclusions of metal, troilite and some lawrencite which oxidizes, discoloring the mass. We also find in ninety per cent of the stones small roundish inclusions of olivine and pyroxenes called chondrules.

The classification of stony meteorites is principally chemical, although it is also associated with their mineralogical structure. There are a few stones which have structures similar to terrestrial basalts; these contain much silicon, few metallic blebs and no chondrules. Their content of radioactive material averages nearly twice that of the other stony meteorites.

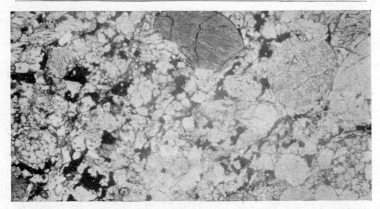

Fig. 97.—Microscopic appearance of the stony meteorite from Bluff, Texas.

The meteorite is a confused mixture of fragmental crystals including many large, nearly spherical grains or chondrules. (*United States National Museum.*)

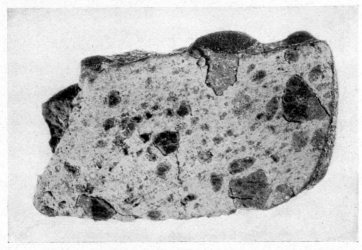

Fig. 98.—Cross-section of the Pasamonte meteorite.

This meteorite, which fell from the spectacular fireball shown in Figure 72, is rich in calcium and free of chondrules, although it contains many irregularily shaped nodules. (*United States National Museum.*)

The stones including chondrules show a great variety of structure. They are principally fragments of olivine and pyroxenes including various amounts of free metal and scattered chondrules, grading from bodies easily broken to fairly tough crystalline masses similar to ordinary rocks.

Fig. 99.—A cross-section of the Cumberland Falls meteorite.

This stony meteorite, which fell in **Kentucky** April 9, 1919, consists of two materials differing greatly in appearance. (*United States National Museum.*)

In these latter the chondrules blend into the surrounding material of olivine and pyroxene and can barely be seen. There are also two types of dark stones, the black chondrites and the carbonaceous meteorites. The black chondrites have typical chemical compositions and internal structures but have probably turned black as the result of being heated.

The carbonaceous stones contain little metal but include many small particles of graphite widely scattered through the material, composing a few per cent of the total mass and making these stones black.

Many stony meteorites appear to be composed of several types of material mixed together. One of the most obvious

Fig. 100.—Structure of a chondrule.

This chondrule of enstatite in the Hendersonville, North Carolina stony meteorite shows a high degree of internal crystal structure. (*Courtesy of E. P. Henderson.*)

examples is the stone that fell at Cumberland Falls, Kentucky in 1919, Figure 99. Here we distinctly see angular black masses imbedded in whitish material of quite different composition. These mixed meteorites and the general fragmental condition of nearly all the stones are extremely difficult to explain.

If we knew how chondrules were formed and how they came to their present positions, we should be much nearer knowing how meteorites originated. The alternatives are few, either the chondrules formed where we find them or they are inclusions. The principal difficulty with having them formed where they are found comes in explaining how they took on their shapes and internal structure while immersed in masses of splintered crystals. If we suppose that the crystals were broken after the chondrules were formed, we must explain how much of the material was shattered yet the chondrules remained intact. G. P. Merrill, of the U. S. National Museum, thought the chondrules were inclusions. He classified them into two groups: oval pseudo-chondrules having a homogeneous internal structure, and the true spherical chondrules having a complex internal crystal structure. The former he thought were just pieces of olivine or pyroxene that were shaped by grinding, like the round pebbles in a stream bed. The spherical chondrules he considered as solidified droplets. Just how, when or where these droplets formed he did not specify nor should he be expected to because this is a problem for the astronomer.

Nearly all stony meteorites include quantities of nickel-iron in the form of veins, flakes, and grains; sometimes the metal encases a silicate crystal or a chondrule. This metal contains an average of nine per cent nickel and is entirely comparable to that comprising the largest metallic meteorites. Even its content of the precious metals is the same as the great metallic meteorites weighing tons. In no stone has a piece of metal been found that is large enough to show Widmanstätten figures, but X-ray analysis reveals the atomic structure of this metal to be identical with that of irons. How it came to be finely divided and nearly uniformly dispersed through the majority of stony meteorites is most perplexing. One authority suggested that it was produced where found through the disintegration of iron-chloride, lawrencite, and that the chlorine escaped, but there is no evidence that the necessary quantities of lawrencite were ever present. Furthermore, this origin would not account for its content of the precious metals. Possibly the metal permeated the silicate in the liquid or gaseous state; but the fragmental, angular silicates show no evidence of having been heated. Some genetic relation between the metal and surrounding silicate is indicated by Prior's observation that when the metal is abundant, it is rich in iron and the silicate rich in magnesium; while as the quantity of metal decreases it becomes richer in nickel and the silicate richer in iron. Yet the fragmental, mixed structure of the silicates hardly suggests that the metal quietly separated from the silicates.

TECTITES

Small glassy particles, called tectites, found in many regions of the earth may be a type of stony meteorite we have not previously recognized. They were first found in Bohemia, but have been turning up in all parts of the world. The regions of the East Indies and Australia contain a great supply, some have been found along the Ivory Coast of Africa while a few have been discovered in South America and recently in Texas. They are a real glass, nearly seventy-five per cent silica, and contain many small bubbles and flow marks as though they had solidified from a liquid. Many of them are shaped like the figure eight or like round buttons, both forms suggesting that they solidified while spinning. A meteoritic origin was suggested long ago by Suess, but only recently has the evidence supporting such a theory become at all convincing. Whatever they are, they deserve closer attention and careful study. If they are meteorites, we have one more peculiar type to add to the several already unexplained.

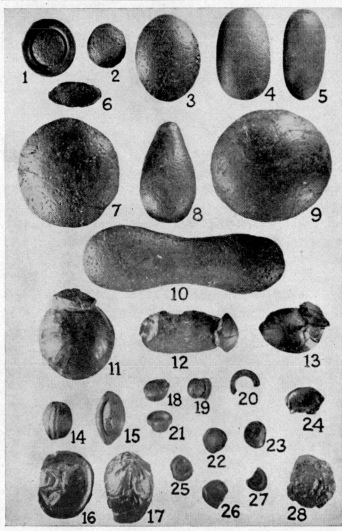

Fig. 101.—Typical tectites.

Part of the Kennett Collection from Australia studied by Charles Fenner of the University of Adelaide. This group, 0.8 times natural size, illustrates the variety of shapes customarily found among tectites, shapes ranging from flanged buttons (1) through oval forms to tear-drops (8) and dumbbells (10).

STONY-IRONS

A small number of meteorites consisting of approximately equal parts stony and metallic materials are called stony-irons. Two types are most frequent; those in which the metal forms a continual mesh, pallasites, and those in which the metal is probably discontinuous, mesosiderites.

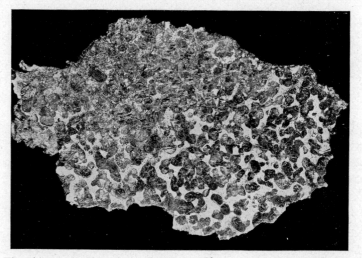

Fig. 102.—A slice of the Brenham, Kansas, stony-iron meteorite.
This meteorite, consisting of nearly equal parts metal, white in the picture, and silicates is classed among the pallasites. (*Thane L. Bierwert, American Museum of Natural History, New York.*)

Wherever sufficiently large surfaces of metal are exposed the Widmanstätten figure appears. Evidently whatever process was responsible for this pattern in the irons has operated upon the stony-irons as well. In the pallasites the silicates are principally dense olivine, while in the mesosiderites they are olivine, pyroxenes and feldspars. The stony-irons range from merely metal and olivine to those having a chondritic structure, and form a definite, but little populated connecting link between the irons and stones. Although the metal and stone are thoroughly intermixed, each completely preserves its normal characteristics.

HISTORY OF STONES

Two theories attempt to explain at least some of the pecularities of stony meteorites. The first, more direct hypothesis forms them by the crystallization of a molten magma but fails to account for their fragmental structure. The presence of chondrules and of metallic inclusions does not fit into such a simple explanation. The second suggestion involves a complicated multiplicity of processes. Material differing considerably in composition and structure must be pulverized, then mixed, chondrules included and the whole compressed into a solid. Yet the orderly variation of structure, composition and metal content are strongly against such a mixing having occurred. Furthermore, the queries of how, when and where such processes took place can be answered only by pyramiding postulates. Neither hypothesis satisfactorily accounts for the observed structure of the stones and we have no idea how they formed. The principal difficulties to a satisfactory answer will be removed when the origins of chondrules and of the free metal and their relations, if any, to the adjacent silicates are better understood.

Since meteorites are continually swinging around the sun, some may venture so near they are intensely heated. We have already noted that three per cent of the stones, apparently typical in composition and structure, have turned black. If this results from heating, we should be able to produce similar changes in the laboratory and when we heat stones to 800°C. for a few minutes they do turn black. Although we are not yet certain that the blackening of the man-made specimens comes from the same causes that blackened those seen to fall, the similarity of appearance is highly suggestive. If the black chondrites are ordinary stones transformed by heating, it probably occurred when they wandered close to some star. We know the immense distances between stars and can easily calculate that any particular meteorite might wander near enough to be baked once in a million million million years. Since the meteorites are only a few thousand million years old, the chances that we would have run into one that had been heated are very small, yet we find that three in every hundred are black, so heating during interstellar wanderings is ruled out. If the sun caused the transformation, the relative infrequency of alteration must be explained. This is not difficult when we note that the high temperatures necessary for the transformation occur only within 0.1 A.U. of the sun and that the great majority of meteorites when they met the earth were moving in orbits with perihelia outside the orbit of Venus. During their past history perturbations probably shuffled their orbits bringing a fraction close to the sun where the heating occurred.

THE AGES OF METEORITES

Geochemists can determine the ages of meteorites and many rocks by carefully measuring their contents of radium and helium. The time-keeper is the pop-corn disintegration of uranium and thorium. In 4560 million years one half of all the uranium atoms and in 13,000 million years one half of all the thorium atoms in the universe explode. Once started on violent careers the atoms progress through a number of forms—radium constitutes one stage in the history of uranium atoms—until finally inert lead is the end-product. During their disintegration the atoms shoot off electrons, hard X-rays and helium atoms. Eight helium atoms come from each uranium atom and six from each thorium. When we know the rate of helium production and the amounts of helium, uranium and thorium in a specimen we have a measure of its age.

TABLE 28
HELIUM-RADIUM AGES OF METEORITES

Name	Type	He*	U†	Age, million years
Cape York, Savik	Om	0.0002	0.6	?
Coahuila	Hex	0.23	0.9	220
Bethany, Goamus	Of	0.43	3.9	100
Nagura	Og	1.19	2.1	470
Seelasgen	Ogg	2.0	14.7	120
Murnpeowie	?	2.0	3.3	520
Mount Joy	Ogg	2.3	2.1	890
Nejed	Om	3.7	3.3	900
Tamarugal	Om	4.0	6.0	550
Cranbourne	Og	4.96	2.4	1600
Toluca	Om	5.82	51.0	100
Arispe	Ogg	7.22	3.9	1500
Narraburra	Off	11.44	5.4	1570
Wichita Co	Og	11.50	3.9	2100
San Angelo	Om	11.86	12.6	800
N'Goureyma	Ob	13.91	8.7	1250
Cosby's Creek	Og	14.0	12.0	930
Hraschina	Om	14.9	7.8	1450
Sacramento Mts	Om	15.03	7.5	1550
Seneca Falls	Om	15.03	6.0	1900
Charcas	Om	15.65	13.2	1000
Staunton III	Om	18.82	6.3	2150
Staunton V	Om	18.92	7.2	2000
Joe Wright Mt	Om	19.28	12.3	1200
Burlington	Om	19.31	10.8	1400
Nelson Co	Ogg	20.0	5.4	2600
Williamstown	Om	20.77	6.3	2400
Lenarto	Om	22.23	6.9	2300
Thundra	Om	28.57	6.9	2800
Mount Ayliff	Og	35.81	8.4	2800

* *Helium in 10^{-6} cc. per gram of meteorite.*
† *Uranium in 10^{-8} gm. per gram of meteorite.*

In meteorites the quantities of radioactive elements are exceedingly small, they are much less abundant than in the average rock of the earth. Delicate electrical tests just reveal these elements in the meteorites and the measurements of their ages is truly an outstanding accomplishment of modern physical chemistry. F. Paneth and his associates who made these measurements proceeded originally on the assumption that little thorium was present in the meteorites and since it decayed more slowly than uranium it would contribute at most only ten per cent of the helium atoms found. On this assumption the age is given approximately by the relationship: Age = He/U × 8.8 million years, where the helium is measured in cubic centimeters per gram and the uranium in grams per gram of sample. The measurements and ages deduced on this assumption appear in Table 28.

TABLE 29

HELIUM-RADIUM-THORIUM AGES OF METEORITES

	Type	He*	U†	Th†	Age, million years
Bethany, Goamus................	Of	0.2	1.2	17	30
San Martin....................	H	1.6	0.6	9	500
Bethany, Amalia...............	Of	3.0	0.9	6	1000

* *Helium* (*as below Table 28*).
† *Uranium and thorium* (*as for uranium below Table 28*).

Recently Paneth has measured both the uranium and thorium as well as the helium in three meteorites and derived their ages, Table 29. Evidently the thorium is more abundant than was previously supposed; unfortunately it is no constant fraction of the uranium content and we can apply no constant correction to the previously determined ages. However, when corrected for the thorium present the greatest ages in Table 28 can scarcely exceed 2,000 million years, which is the age of the earth measured by the same

technique. Inasmuch as helium is a chemically inert gas
which will escape from a liquid, such helium-ages measure
the interval since the meteorites were molten.

The leakage of helium might completely invalidate these
results, but Paneth found that upon heating coarse filings of
metallic meteorites to 1000°C. for three hours they lost less
than five per cent of their helium. It is securely enmeshed
in the nickel-iron crystals and cannot escape. Stony meteorites contain more radioactive material than do the irons,
but their shattered silicate crystals may have let much of
the helium escape and this technique may not give accurate
ages for them. Nevertheless sufficient helium was found in
two stones, Pultusk and Waconda, to indicate ages of several
hundred million years.

Tables 28 and 29 reveal much more than merely the ages
of the oldest meteorites. Each shows a range of ages, a range
from the age of the earth to almost the geological present.
This apparent recent solidification of some of the meteorites
and the unbroken sequence from the oldest to the youngest,
a sequence apparently independent of any characteristic of
the metal, are more perplexing and difficult to explain than
the maximum age.

ORIGIN OF METEORITES

Having surveyed the composition and structure of
meteorites we may speculate how they came into existence.
Our astronomical knowledge proves their extraterrestrial
origin, but is not definite regarding their permanent membership in the solar system. Chemically the two types of
material, stony and metallic, show minor variations, but
each forms a continuous sequence from the highly chondritic
stones rich in metal to the metal-free achondrites, and from
the nickel-poor to the nickel-rich ataxites. Between the
stones and irons certain chemical distinctions are almost
complete, for example, the concentration of the precious

metals in the nickel-iron and the radioactive elements in the silicate. Yet the distinct metallic and silicate phases are united by the stony-irons and the similarity of the free metal wherever found. All this evidence shows that the stony and metallic meteorites form a single continuous sequence of material which must have had a common origin.

Among the unlikely hypotheses for the origin of meteorites is that of volcanic action on the moon. We are, however, inclined to place their origin much farther from the earth and consider some mechanisms that could have produced them. The alternatives are few: they may have grown in space through the accumulation of individual atoms, they may have grown in space through the accumulation of small bits of solid material, or they may be fragments of some solid body comparable to a planet.

In interplanetary and interstellar space are atoms of hydrogen, sodium, calcium, titanium and probably most other elements. Recently molecules involving carbon and nitrogen have been discovered between the stars, and other molecules, such as water, probably exist there. These molecules may occasionally band together to form tiny nuclei which pick up other stray atoms and eventually build up a dust particle in space. But we need only recall the complex chemical and physical structure of meteorites to realize that they were not built up by the accumulation of individual atoms.

The fragmental structure of stony meteorites might be explained by the aggregation of solid particles. Yet, unless we make some weird guess about the distribution of material in space, the orderly array of chemical and mineral structure among both stones and irons is strongly against any such origin. We might extrapolate the evidence from meteor spectra and argue that stony meteorites were members of the solar system while the more uniform metallic particles came from between the stars. This again neglects completely the continuity of structure between stones and irons. Moreover, the segregation and crystal structure of certain compounds, troilite, schreibersite and cohenite which sometimes are neatly encased in kamacite, conflicts with the origin of the irons through the accumulation of atoms or particles. Their structure could develop only upon slow cooling from a liquid.

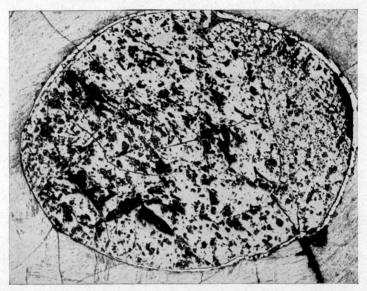

Fig. 103.—A troilite inclusion.

In the Canyon City meteorite, an octahedrite, is this typical troilite inclusion bounded by a thin border of swathing kamacite. The black spots are surface imperfections due to the difficulties of polishing the brittle troilite; 83 times original. (*Stuart H. Perry.*)

This chemical and mineralogical homogeneity and continuity demand an origin for all meteorites under essentially similar conditions. Presumably this would be as a single body, yet throughout space physical conditions and processes may be so uniform that indistinguishable material would form. If meteorites move in hyperbolic orbits, this last condition cannot be escaped, for the variety of motions and velocities means that we are dealing with the fragmental remains of a great number of different bodies. It is more probable that meteorites developed as a single cooling mass comparable in size to the earth.

A SMALL PLANET

Analogies between meteorites and the deep structure of the earth are readily named, but we must consider them carefully noting the discordant as well as the favorable facts. At the center of the earth is a large core extending more than half way to the surface and having a density eleven or twelve times that of water. If relieved of the compression of the overlying materials, this core would have a density near eight, comparable to that of metallic meteorites. Seismograms reveal, however, that the outer part of the core has very little strength and behaves like a liquid; but there is some indication that the central part of the core may be solid. If this is the situation, we see how some metallic meteorites at the center of such a core, might have been solid almost from the origin of the planet while others in the same body remained liquid for many hundred million years.

Surrounding the earth's core are very basic silicates probably similar in composition to stony meteorites. How and why the silicate and metallic materials of meteorites or of the earth would separate has been studied extensively by V. M. Goldschmidt and others. They conclude that from a great molten mixture having the composition of the earth, the silicates would separate from the metal and float to the top like slag on molten iron. The atoms of the precious metals, having nearly the same size as the atoms of nickel and iron, would be trapped in the metal. As the silicate material cooled, the dense rocks, olivine and pyroxene, having the highest melting points, would solidify first and

lie adjacent to the metal. As the process of separation continued the final slag forming the outer crust would be rich
in silica, forming granite, and have a high concentration of
the radioactive elements, as we find in the earth's crust.
Any layer intermediate between the metallic core and the
silicates would presumably consist of intermixed metal and
silicates.

Such a sequence of material is represented by the nickel-
iron masses; the stony-irons varying from the pallasites, rich
in metal and olivine, through the mesosiderites with less
metal and more acidic silicates, to the various classes of
stones with decreasing metal and increasing silica content.
This sequence of meteorites is too complete to be accidental
and must be attributed to a process of separation like that
which brings the cream to the top of the milk bottle. Such
an analogy is, however, based entirely upon chemical data.
The equally important mineralogical evidence suggests
that the irons cooled at an exceedingly low rate during
which their large crystal structure developed. At the center
of a cooling mass this is exactly what we might expect to
have happen. The heterogeneous, fragmental structure of
the stones with their chondrules present the greatest dis-
crepancy with such an origin. If we could show that the
stones took on their present structure while under high
pressure deep within a sizable mass or when it was disrupted, our difficulties in formulating a comprehensive and
coherent explanation would be greatly diminished. Like
the scientists of the past century, we shall remain at a stale-
mate unless we can penetrate and understand the structure
of the stony meteorites.

We have compared the hypothetical parent of the meteorites with the earth and the other inner planets. When we
examine these planets we find a most puzzling relation
between density and size (Table 30). The moon has the

TABLE 30
RELATION BETWEEN SIZE AND DENSITY OF MOON AND SMALL PLANETS

	Diameter, km	Density
Moon.....................................	3,480	3.33
Mercury..................................	5,000	3.8
Mars.....................................	6,770	3.96
Venus....................................	12,400	4.86
Earth....................................	12,700	5.52

density of ordinary silicates under low pressure and it can contain no appreciable quantity of dense metal as a core. Mercury and Mars may have small cores but whether they are metallic or composed of dense compressed silicates is uncertain. The earth, however, has a sizable dense core and presumably Venus does also. If meteorites came from a planet-like body, it must have been comparable to the earth in size, otherwise it would have had no core from which to produce metallic meteorites.

Meteorites are almost certainly fragments of some large body which we are tempted to identify also as the progenitor of the asteroids. The meteorites tell little about how or where it was shattered, but their least ages suggest a recent catastrophe, almost too recent. One so recent that there may not have been time for the asteroids to attain their present orbital arrangement through perturbations. Some part of their organization may, however, have been inherited from the parent's orbit. The recent discovery of small asteroids moving in orbits similar to those of fireballs proves that the orbits of all these interplanetary particles are interwoven; we cannot distinguish a large meteorite from a small asteroid. To better understand the interplanetary material we must obtain all possible information from meteorites, our only physical clues.

10

BETWIXT AND BETWEEN

In the preceding chapters we have discussed comets, asteroids, and meteors and found that millions of small bodies are continually moving in and out among the planets. In this chapter we shall consider this vast assemblage of particles as a single great cloud of diffuse material stretching throughout the solar system. We may wonder if this aggregation of interplanetary wanderers, each reflecting a tiny amount of sunlight, reveals itself as a general illumination of the night sky. If we stand on a clear moonless evening watching the western sky, we may notice a faint band of light extending upward from the place where the sun has set. Perhaps this is part of the Milky Way, but no, the Milky Way extends in a north-south direction, while this band of light has the shape of a cone pointing up along the zodiac. If we happen to be early risers, or are very curious, we shall see for ourselves that a similar cone of light, sometimes called the false dawn, appears in the eastern sky before true dawn begins.

The Light of the Sky

This morning and evening illumination is the zodiacal light, which keen-eyed observers claim to trace completely

Fig. 104.—The Zodiacal light.

A painting by Hubert Jarvis shows the zodiacal light as observed from Queensland, Australia on July 31, 1936. (*Reproduced from the Memoirs of the British Astronomical Association.*)

across the sky. It is most intense near the sun and gradually fades away farther around the zodiac. From the temperate latitudes the zodiacal light can be seen under favorable conditions and is most obvious when the zodiac rises vertically from the horizon. From the latitudes of the United States the evening light is best seen during March and April, while the morning light is most conspicuous during September and October. At other times of the year the zodiac meets the horizon at small angles and the brighter part of the light is obliterated by atmospheric absorption and dust along the horizon. From the tropics the zodiac always stands nearly vertical and the zodiacal light is quite intense and conspicuous.

Just opposite the sun the faint band of light becomes more intense, appearing as a large hazy area, termed the counterglow, eight to ten degrees long and five to seven degrees wide. Almost anyone who is well away from city lights can see the zodiacal light at the most favorable times of year, but only the most keen-eyed observers detect the large diffuse counterglow.

Over the whole sky is a faint luminosity not due to the myriads of stars too faint to be seen individually. This night sky light consists of numerous atomic radiations, some of which are greatly intensified in brilliant aurorae. One radiation in the green gives the majority of aurorae their soft greenish color. Evidently some of the night sky light comes from a faint permanent aurora produced high in the atmosphere by atoms releasing energy they have stored up during the day. Since we view the zodiacal light through this luminous atmosphere, a part of the zodiacal light must be sky light, but the major portion of it comes from farther in space.

The spectrum of the zodiacal light contains not only bright lines emitted by the permanent aurorae, but also a continuous band of color that must be reflected sunlight. This might be reflected from gas atoms circling far above the earth, from gas atoms between the earth and sun, or from the millions of meteors swinging around the sun. None of these possible explanations require much material; the density of the zodiacal material is about what we would get if we stretched a thimble filled with air until it formed a column reaching from the earth to the sun. This small amount of stuff, enough to provide the zodiacal light, blocks off less than a millionth of the light coming to the earth from a distant star. While many atoms and molecules of gas may be roaming between the earth and sun, we know that millions of meteors are there. The sunlight reflected from these separate bodies, whose orbits have low inclinations, add up as a faint glow along the plane of the planetary motions, just as a rainbow is formed by the light sent back from innumerable water droplets forming a spring shower.

One simple observation eliminates the possibility of reflection by gas atoms and molecules. They are notoriously selective in the color of light they scatter; just notice that the sunlit sky is blue while the sunlight falling upon it is yellowish. The gas and dust in the atmosphere scatter the blue light over the sky and make the sun appear yellower than it really is. Since the color of the zodiacal light is almost exactly that of sunlight, it must be reflected from particles larger than gas molecules or bits of dust.

Whether or not the meteors can reflect enough light to account for the observed brightness of the zodiacal light depends entirely upon how many meteors there are in space and how large they are. A few large particles will not send us much light, but the same bodies broken into fragments will appear much brighter. If we turn back to Table 19 and find the total area of each magnitude group of meteors, we realize that the numerous small bodies have vastly more reflecting surface than the large ones—a peck of little potatoes has a much greater surface to be peeled than a peck of large potatoes. When the meteors' surfaces are added up and assumed to reflect light with the same efficiency as the moon, we find that in the direction forty degrees from the sun they should send us about as much light per square degree as one or two stars of the fifth magnitude. This value is surprisingly close to the zodiacal brightness as measured by Elvey with a photoelectric photometer.

These particles are not only between the earth and sun, but are also scattered throughout space at least as far as the orbit of Jupiter. Those beyond the earth's orbit reflect sunlight towards us, and, if they behave like the moon at full phase, those exactly opposite the sun send back an extra high fraction of the light falling upon them. Thus in the direction opposite the sun the zodiacal light should brighten into the hazy spot which we see as the counterglow.

If the zodiacal light is reflected sunlight, it should be polarized like the light from the asteroids, moon and planets. Dufay and others found that at angles between thirty and sixty degrees from the sun the zodiacal light is twelve per cent polarized, but at larger angles the polarization drops rapidly until it is only three per cent at right angles to the sun. To reconcile these observations with the polarizing ability of rocks, which have a maximum near quarter-phase, we must, in Figure 105, place the reflecting particles well away from the earth.

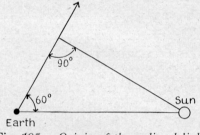

Fig. 105.—Origin of the zodiacal light.

Light from the sun falls on particles between the planets and is reflected. As seen from the earth this light forms a narrow band extending along the zodiac.

The general light of the night sky has a maximum of polarization of a few per cent at the same angles from the sun as does the zodiacal light. We interpret this polarization to mean that about fifteen per cent of the general light of the night sky is sunlight reflected from meteors moving in inclined orbits which carry them well above and below the plane of planetary motions.

OTHER POINTS OF VIEW

Since we know the general way in which the interplanetary particles move, we may visualize how they would appear as seen from other planets, for example Mercury,

Mars, Jupiter and Pluto. From atmosphere-less Mercury, close to the sun, the zodiacal light would be much brighter

Fig. 106.—The interplanetary material.

This remarkable photograph, made February 13, 1941 by the Texas Observers, shows the cone of the zodiacal light extending towards Jupiter and Saturn in the upper right corner. Comet 1941c with its bright tail extending nearly vertically is in the center of the picture. The irregularities of brightness in the zodiacal light are spurious and result from the great contrast used to bright out faint details. (*The Texas Observers, Fort Worth, Texas.*)

and extend around the sky to form an easily-seen counter-glow. Few comets would venture near and those that did would shoot past quickly. The asteroids would be faint and

many that we can observe from the earth would not be
known. Because Mercury has little or no protecting atmosphere meteors must strike its surface with their full force,
continually blasting craters ranging in size from pin-pricks
to gaping pits. As a result of their high speed near the sun
and the lack of an air-cushion, nearly all meteorites must
be destroyed at impact.

The terrestrial astronomer transported to Mars would
find the celestial scenery only slightly different in appearance. Perhaps the greatest change would be the increased
faintness of the zodiacal light, which would be very difficult
to observe. From Mars, almost in the asteroid zone, these
little planets would be bright and easily observed. A few
comets of large perihelion distance which remain too faint
to be seen from the earth might be discovered. Rarely
would a bright comet having a long tail be well placed for
observation, because long tails grow only when a comet is
near the sun. From Mars the majority would be lost against
the bright sky of twilight. Numerous short-period comets
pass close by Mars and meteor showers originating from
them may be more numerous than on the earth. Sporadic
meteors and meteorites may be a little more abundant but
less conspicuous because their orbital velocities are lower
than when meeting the earth.

From Jupiter our picture of the solar system and especially of the interplanetary material would be greatly
changed. For example the earth would never appear more
than eleven degrees from the sun—much closer than Mercury is to the sun as seen from the earth. The zodiacal light,
comet tails and other phenomena occurring near the sun
would be practically unknown. Although a multitude of
asteroids would be visible, they would not be as conspicuous
as seen from Mars, for when nearest they present their
shadowed side to the observer. Just how Jupiter effects the

capture of the short-period comets and how many of these move around the sun would be quite apparent to the Jovian astronomer, for he is at the source of the action and can watch it progress. Both sporadic meteors and meteor showers must appear frequently, due as much to the great gravitational attraction of Jupiter as to its location far out in the interplanetary material.

From distant Pluto, nearly forty times as far from the sun as we are on the earth, the interplanetary material would hardly be known. The zodiacal light and ordinary asteroids would be quite unknown. Comets passing near by would consist of meteor swarms surrounded by perhaps a little dimly illuminated gas; at best they would be difficult to observe and relatively uninteresting. Only in one respect would an astronomer on Pluto have an advantage over those on the earth—he could tell what fraction of meteors originate in interstellar space, for at this great solar distance the parabolic velocity is only seven kilometers per second and meteors coming from interstellar space would move much faster and could easily be identified.

In the Beginning

What part the interplanetary particles played in the origin and early history of the solar system we can only surmise. When we worry about how they, and the whole solar system, came into existence, we must not forget that the asteroids, comets and meteors are interrelated. Moreover, we cannot neglect these millions of particles when discussing how the planets themselves were formed.

Throughout the preceding chapters we have tried to organize our knowledge of each type of interplanetary traveler and to see what type of origin best accounted for the observations. We might attempt to go even farther, outlining how these processes could have arisen when the solar

system was formed or in the intervening ages. Such speculation hardly seems profitable, for we lack much essential
information about each type of body in the system. Already
we have many conflicting and contradictory conclusions to
disentangle. Some of the contradictions may result from
errors in our interpretation of the available observations,
but they may also result from our incomplete and distorted
information. On some subjects, like the motions of the
asteroids, our knowledge is very precise; on other subjects,
like the velocities of meteors, it is sadly inaccurate.

Outstanding Questions

We cannot end this short summary of our present knowledge of the bodies between the planets without listing some
of the pertinent questions that remain unanswered:

Do asteroids move in the zone between Jupiter and
Saturn?

Where do the asteroids leave off and meteors begin?

How did great clusters of small stony particles originally
band together to become comets?

If the shower meteors are stony particles, what is the
origin of metallic meteors and meteorites?

How many comets come to perihelion near the orbit of
Jupiter and remain invisible to us?

Do all meteors belong to the solar system or do some
originate between the stars?

How did stony meteorites acquire their peculiar internal
structure?

What are the true inter-relationships between comets,
meteors, meteorites and asteroids?

INDEX

215

S

T

U

V

W

Z